HAND BOOK OF MEDICAL HISTOLOGY

(with points for slide identification)

Dedicated to the Students who find romance in Anatomy

HAND BOOK OF MEDICAL HISTOLOGY

(with points for slide identification)

Dr. R. K. Ghosh

Ex-Professor of Anatomy

CURRENT BOOKS INTERNATIONAL

60, Lenin Sarani, Kolkata – 700 013

FIRST PUBLISHED - OCTOBER, 2016

Price in India : Rs. 200.00

Publisher

CURRENT BOOKS INTERNATIONAL
60, Lenin Sarani, Kolkata – 700 013
☎ (033) 2249 2226, Cell : 9433087322
E-mail : currentbooksinternational@gmail.com

Distributor

MEDICAL BOOK COMPANY PVT. LTD.
34, Sir Nilratan Sarkar Sarani (Creek Row), Kolkata – 700 014
☎ (033) 2249 1435, Cell : 9432072758, Tele-Fax : (91) 033-2227 6980
E-mail : mbckolkata@bsnl.in ; mbcplkolkata@gmail.com

Branches

Bangalore	Lakshmi Complex (1st Floor), 40, K. R. Road, Opp. Vani Vilas Hospital, Bangalore – 560 002 ; ✆ (080) 26707525, E-mail : mbcplbangalore@gmail.com ; mbcbangalore@bsnl.in
Coimbatore	99B, Avinashi Road, Opp. Coimbatore Medical College Coimbatore – 641 014 ✆ (0422) 2590588, E-mail : mbccoimbatore@bsnl.in
Hyderabad	M.C.H. Complex (Ground Floor), Shop No. 9 & 10, Putli Bowli, Kothi, Hyderabad – 500 095 ; ✆ (040) 24651038, E-mail : mbchyderabad@gmail.com ; mbchyderabad@bsnl.in
Nagpur	Plot No. 79, Rambag Layout (1st Floor) Opp. Medical College, Nagpur – 440 003 ✆ (0712) 2741921, E-mail : mbcnagpur@bsnl.in
Vadodara	Vinraj Plaza, Opp. Govt. Press, Kothi Road Vadodara – 390 001 ; ✆ (0265) 2422789, E-mail : mbcbaroda@gmail.com ; mbcbaroda@dataone.in

Printed by : **The Indian Press Pvt. Ltd.**, Kolkata

ISBN - 978-93-85274-19-0

Website : www.currentbooksint.com

Preface

This hand book of Medical Histology has been prepared with precise information and illustrations on the basis of the problems frequently encountered by the 1st year medical students, particularly during the time of examination.

Coloured photomicrographs of about 40 stained slides of the tissues of various organs have been presented with desired magnifications along with some line-drawings to facilitate better understanding to the students of undergraduate level. Photomicrographs have been carefully selected out of numerous tissue slides, prepared by the author himself. Specific identification points have been provided under each of the photographs as per the characteristics of the tissues as well as their appearances under light microscope.

The text of the book has been written in simple and easy language without going into unnecessary details to avoid confusion. This endeavour will be successful if this hand book becomes useful to the students and teachers of this subject.

The author expresses his gratitude to Dr. Asim Kumar Datta, his philosopher and guide who has kindly allowed to take some illustrations from his publications.

The author expresses thanks to Mrs. Sarbani Bhattacharya, Mr. Aninda Bhattacharya and Mr. Chiranjit Burman of Current Books International, Kolkata for the publication of this book and for providing technical support respectively.

The encouragement of Dr. Rekha Ghosh (wife), Gargi Ghosh (daughter) and Arnab Ghosh (son) with regard to this publication is hereby acknowledged.

The author also thankful to Dr. P. Das and Dr. S. Ray for providing facility for documentation of tissue slides.

945, Block-A, Lake Town
Kolkata – 89

R. K. Ghosh

Acknowledgements

Elias, H.E., Pauly, J.E. and Burns, E.R. (1978) : Histology and Human Microanatomy, 4th Edn., Piccin Medical Books, Padova, Italy.

Williams, P.L. and Warwick, R. (1980) : Grey's Human Anatomy, 36th Edn., Churchill Livingstone, Edinburgh London Melbourne and New York.

Ghosh, S. and Anbalagan, J. (1998) : Essentials of Histology, 1st Edn., Current Books International, Kolkata, India.

Chatterjee, C.C. (1985) : Human Physiology, Volume-I, 11th Edn., Medical Allied Agency, M.G. Road, Kolkata, India.

Mahapatra, A.B.S. (2012) : Essentials of Medical Physiology, 3rd Edn., Current Books International, Kolkata, India.

Datta, A.K. (2015) : Functional Histology, 1st Edn., Current Books International, Kolkata, India.

Contents

List of Histological Slides (Photomicrograph) with Points for Identification

1
ANIMAL CELL

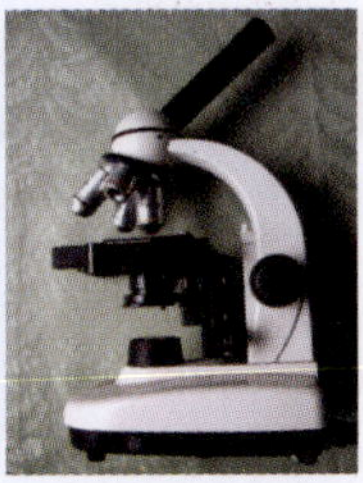

A cell is a mass of protoplasm enclosed in a semi-permeable membrane and forms the basic structural and functional unit of all tissues and organs in the animal body.

The cells which do not possess any organized nucleus are known as **Prokaryotic** cells and nucleated cells are called **Eukaryotic** cells. Some bacteria and blue-green algae are the examples of prokaryotic cells and most of the cells in the animal body are eukaryotic.

Functionally two types of cells are available in the animal body :

(a) Somatic cells – These cells form various organs of the body and contain diploid (2n) number of chromosomes.

(b) Reproductive cells – They take part in the reproduction and contain haploid (n) number of chromosomes. Reproductive cells are of two types – i) Male reproductive cells or male gametes or spermatozoa and ii) Female reproductive cells or female gametes or ova.

- Eukaryotic cells
  - Somatic cells
  - Reproductive cells
    - Male reproductive cells [Spermatozoa]
    - Female reproductive cells [Ova]

STRUCTURE OF A CELL

This structural unit of the living body may be of various shapes or sizes. They may be flat or cubical or pyramidal or columnar or irregular in shape. The size (diameter) ranges from 5 to 50 microns in most of the somatic cells. However, female reproductive cells and nerve cells are bigger in size.

Irrespective of shape and size each cell comprises of a cell membrane, cytoplasm and a nucleus.

Cell Membrane

Each cell is covered by a thin semipermeable membrane called cell membrane or plasma membrane. Generally it is 70Å thick and is composed of three layers of materials. Outer and inner layers are formed by protein and intermediate layer is composed of lipid. The ***lipids*** are mainly phospho lipids. The phospholipid molecules are arranged in double layer with hydrophilic end (polar) at the periphery and hydrophobic end at the middle.

The ***proteins*** not only present at the outer as well as inner surfaces but pierce the membrane through and through and forms water channels, ion channels, different pumps, receptors and enzymes. The cell membrane performs the following functions :

i) Maintains the shape of the cell.

ii) Helps in the selective interchange of inorganic ions.

iii) It allows selective permeability to lipid molecules.

iv) It accommodates various receptors.

v) The membrane helps intake of fluid inside cell cytoplasm by the way of pinocytosis.

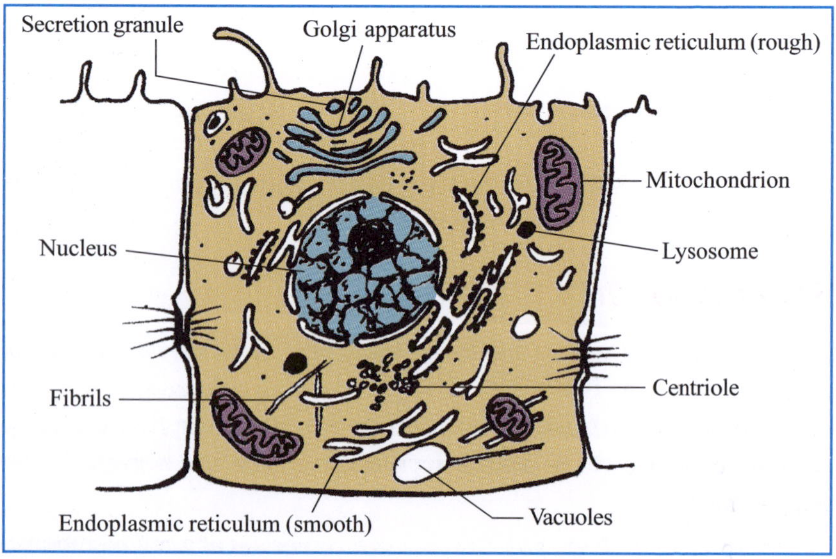

Fig. 1.1

Intercellular connections

The cells are held together by means of connections and help in communications between cells.

a) **Tight junction** (zonulae occludens) – Here the cell membranes are closely and tightly bound together by ridge like structures contributed by both the adjacent cells. They are found in intestinal mucosa and renal tubules.

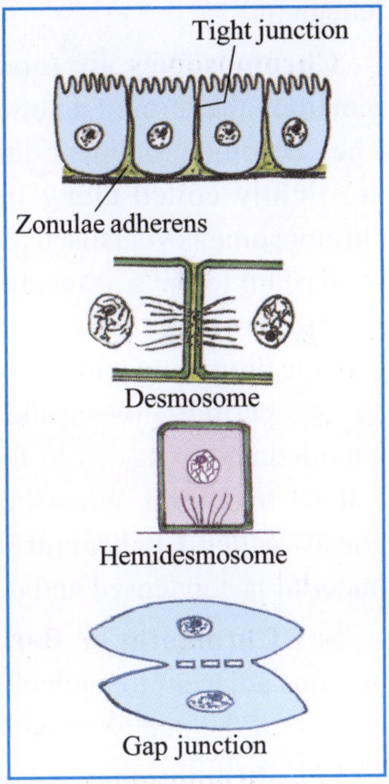

Fig. 1.2

b) **Zonulae adherens** – The cell membranes of these areas are not tightly attached with each other but remain in close apposition. They are present in the epithelia in continuation with tight junctions.

c) **Desmosomes** – These are small areas where adjacent membranes become thickened and the space in between become filled with filament like threads. These filaments radiate to the interior of the cells.

d) **Hemidesmosomes** – When a cell in placed on a basement membrane, a half of the desmosome is found on the basal surface of the cell.

e) **Cell adhesion molecules** (CAMs) – There are some protein molecules in some specialised junctions. They take part in inflammations, wound healing and in metastasis of tumours.

f) **Gap junction** – There are some gaps or pores in the adjacent membranes of two cells and allow passages of ion, sugar, amino acid, chemical messengers etc.

Nucleus

This is a spherical dense body within the cytoplasm and composed of nuclear membrane, chromosomes, nucleolus and nuclear sap. Its shape, size, position and number may vary. It is absent in mature RBC.

The **Nuclear membrane** is structurally similar to that of cell membrane but is thicker and have few pores. The outer surface of the membrane is sometimes blended with rough surfaced endoplasmic reticulum.

Chromosomes are thread like deeply stained (basic) structures remain in the form of a network within the nucleus at the resting stage. They become prominent during the time of cell division because they are tightly coiled along its entire length and therefore individual chromosome is visualised and identified. The number of chromosomes is constant to the species. In somatic cells the number is 46 in man. In mature germ cells this number will be half (haploid). The chromosomes become prominent with the onset of prophase. But during the interphase i.e. the period between the cell divisions the chromosomes become uncoiled and extended to form a diffuse network. This is collectively called **Chromatin**. When the chromatin material is dispersed and stained poorly, called **Euchromatin**. On the other hand, when the chromatin material is condensed and deeply stained, called **Heterochromatin**.

Sex Chromatin or Barr body – It is a small chromatin material remains adjacent to nucleolus of nerve cell and other cells at the inner surface of the nuclear membrane of female animals.

Sex-chromosomes are only one pair of chromosomes responsible for sex determination. In female, the sex chromosomes are equal in length and are symbolised by XX. In male the sex chromosomes are unequal in length and symbolised by XY. The X represents longer chromosome and Y represents shorter chromosome. Each chromosome presents a constriction known as centromere or kinetocore.

Autosomes – Chromosomes other than sex-chromosomes are called Autosomes. They generally occur in pairs in somatic cells and singly in gamets. Autosomes regulate body character.

The main component of a chromosome is DNA. The genes which are responsible for transmitting the hereditary character are located within the DNA molecule.

Nucleolus is another small body within the nucleus. The number of nucleoli may be more than one in one nucleus. It disappears during prophase and reappears during telephase of cell division. It has no covering and composed of a compressed mass of a mixture of RNA (ribosome) granules and proteins. The RNA granules are liberated from the nucleus and appears in the cytoplasm through nuclear pores.

The **Nuclear sap** is the fluid component of the nucleus and serves as a medium for transportation of RNA.

Cytoplasm

It is the semisolid jelly like substance which remains around the nucleus and enclosed by plasma membrane. This substance is colloid in nature and composed of water, salts, carbohydrates lipids and Ribonuclic acids. The main contents of the cytoplasm may be grouped as follows :

Active elements (organelles)	**Cytoplasmic inclusions**
Endoplasmic reticulum	Food granules –
Golgi body	[Carbohydrate, Protein, Fat]
Mitochondria	Pigments
Lysosomes	Secretion granules
Ribosome granules	
Centrioles	
Fibrils	

Endoplasmic Reticulum

These are membrane bound tubules or vesicles remain in the cytoplasm separately or in the form of network. They are of two types – Smooth surfaced and rough surfaced.

Ribosome particles are attached to the surface of the tubules or the vesicles of rough surfaced Endoplasmic Reticula (rER) and help in protein synthesis. The smooth surfaced Endoplasmic Reticula (sER) help lipid and steroid synthesis. An endoplasmic reticulum tubule may extend from cell membrane to nuclear membrane.

Golgi body / Golgi apparatus

This structure is composed of flat vesicles, secretary vesicles and micro vesicles. It is generally located close to the nucleus. The flat round vesicles are placed one after another and therefore in tissue sections it appears as a stack of tubules. The peripheral parts of these vesicles are little distended.

Actually the secretory vesicles are formed from these distended parts of the flat vesicles and move towards the peripheral surface of the cells. The micro vesicles are small in size and are generally located on the opposite surface of the stacked vesicles.

The protein molecules which are synthesized in the rER are carried by the micro vesicles to the flat vesicles. From the flat vesicles they go to secretory vesicles. The contents of the secretory vesicles are released at the cell surface as zymogen granules.

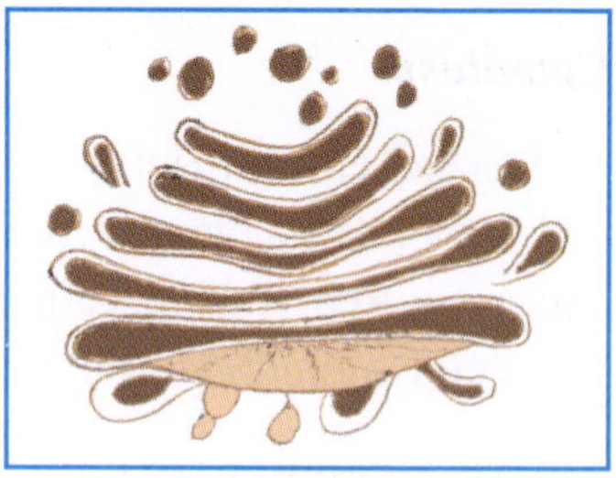

Fig. 1.3

Mitochondria

These are small elongated double walled structures scattered throughout the cytoplasm. The inner membrane forms shelf like projections into the cavity of the organelle by making folds by itself. These shelves are known as **Cristae**. The fluid which is filling the cavity of a mitochondrion is known as matrix. The matrix contains enzymes of Kreb's citric acid cycle, respiratory enzymes, oxidative phosphorylase, etc. The number of this organelle is variable in different tissues. The number is more in Liver, Heart, and Kidneys due to requirement of more energy in these tissues.

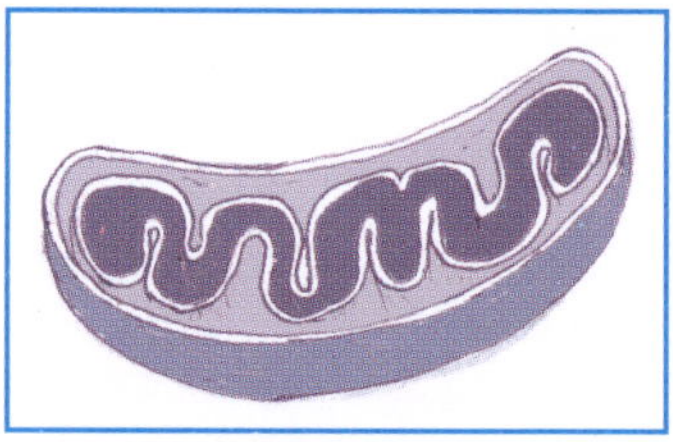

Fig. 1.4

Lysosomes

These are round or oval membrane bound bodies and contain hydrolytic enzymes like lipases, proteases, nucleases, phosphatases, etc. These enzymes can digest substances which enter the cell from outside and the substances which originate from its own cellular materials. They are absent in RBC. They are also called **suicidal bags**, because they will destroy the cell itself if their contents (enzymes) are released within the cell.

Ribosomes

These small granules having diameter of about 100Å and are scattered throughout the cytoplasm either in free form or are attached to the surface of the endoplasmic reticulum. These are actually Ribonucleoprotein granules and help in the protein synthesis. They first appear in the nucleus and pass out to the cytoplasm through the pores of nuclear membrane.

Centrioles

Centrosome is a dense zone of cytoplasm and remains close to the nucleus. It contains two dark particles known as centrioles. Each centriole is composed of an empty tubule formed by nine longitudinal bundles, each of which is made up of three microtubules.

Centrioles form spindle fibers during mitosis. Generally two centrioles are found in all cells which are capable of division.

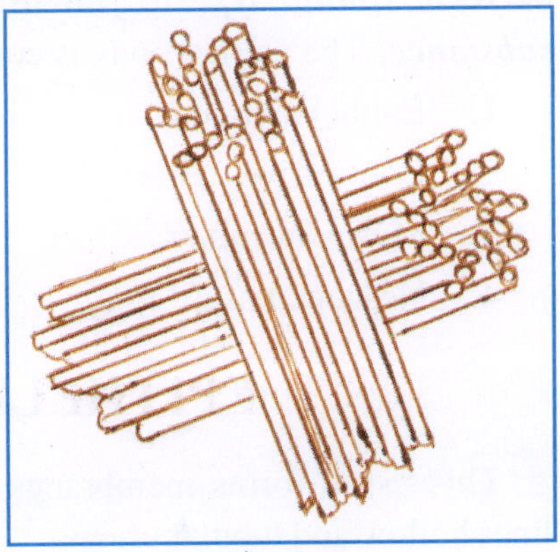

Fig. 1.5

Fibriles and filaments or Plasmosins

These are very fine filamentus structures form a network to give internal support to the cell. They are better developed in muscle cells, nerve cells and epithelial cells. They are formed by lengthwise joining of protein particles rich in Deoxyribonucleoprotein. These fibrils are called **Myofibrils** in muscle cells, **Neurofibrils** in nerve cells and **Tonofibrils** in epithelial cells.

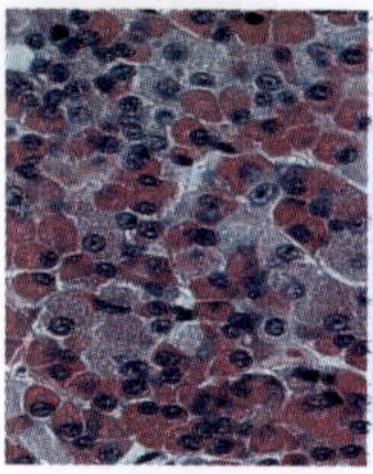

2
TISSUES OF THE BODY

The term tissue is derived from a French word which means texture or weave. Therefore anything looks like a woven material was called tissue. ***The tissue can be defined as a collection of similar cells which perform similar type of function and are united by intercellular substance.*** The animal body is composed of four elementary tissues.

1. Epithelial tissue
2. Connective tissue
3. Muscular tissue
4. Nervous tissue

EPITHELIAL TISSUE

This tissue forms membranes and covers free surfaces as well as lines hollow and tubular organs.

It possesses following characters :

1. The cells rest on a basement membrane which is attached to the basal surface of the epithelial cell and is composed of a basement lamina and a reticular lamina.
2. The cells are closely packed and the intercellular substance is minimum.
3. The non attached surface of the epithelium always remains free.
4. It is non vascular and gets nourishment from the blood vessels of the underlying lamina propria.

The epithelial tissue protects the animal body or an organ and helps in absorption, secretion and excretion.

According to the number of cell layers the epithelial tissue can be divided into different sub-groups.

(a) Simple epithelium
(b) Compound epithelium
(c) Transitional epithelium

SIMPLE EPITHELIUM

When a single layer of cells are arranged on a basement membrane is called simple epithelium. According to the shape of these cells, the simple epithelium may be of following types :

A. Simple squamous epithelium

B. Simple cuboidal epithelium

C. Simple columnar epithelium

D. Simple columnar ciliated epithelium

E. Glandular epithelium

A. Simple squamous epithelium :

This epithelium is made up of a single layer of flat cells placed tightly on a basement membrane. Other than protection it helps easy passage of liquid and gasses and has a dialyzing or filtering function. This epithelium forms serous membrane, alveoli of lungs, loops of Henle, Bowmans capsule, inner lining of heart and vessels. ***Endothelium*** is a term which is used for such an epithelium which lines vessels and similarly the lining epithelium of serous cavities (pleura, peritoneum, etc.) are called **Mesothelium**.

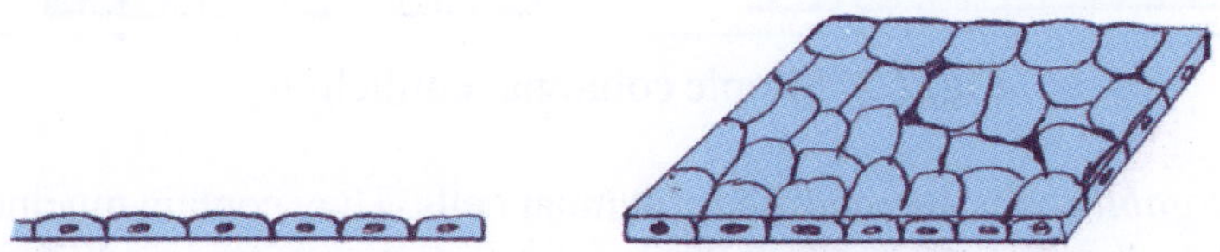

Fig. 2.1 Simple squamous epithelium.

B. Simple cuboidal epithelium :

It is made up of a single layer of cube like cells placed on a thin basement membrane. Other than protection it has secretory and storage property. This epithelium is available in salivary glands, thyroid, terminal respiratory bronchioles etc. In the proximal convoluted tubule, this epithelium possesses longitudinal striation at their free borders, and called brush bordered epithelium. The striation is due to the presence of finger like projections (microvilli) which is designed to increase absorptive surface.

Fig. 2.2 Simple cuboidal epithelium.

C. Simple columnar epithelium :

It is formed by a single layer of cylindrical cells placed on a basement membrane. Each cell have a round nucleus at the centre or towards the basement membrane. The main function of this epithelium is absorption and secretion. They are found in stomach, intestine, gall bladder, etc.

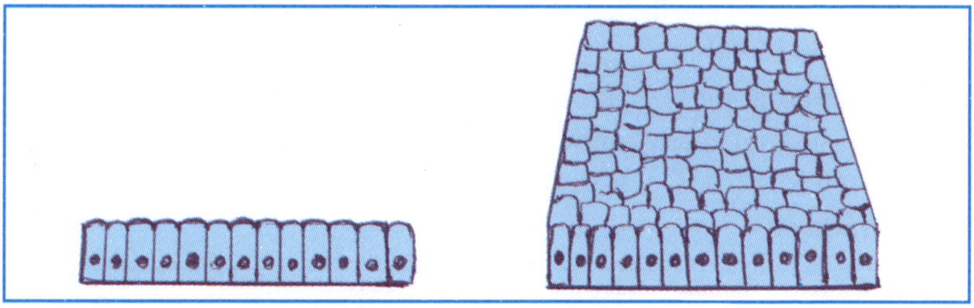

Fig. 2.3 Simple columnar epithelium.

The ***goblet*** cells are modified columnar cells. They contain mucinogen granules close to their free surfaces. When the number of granules increases the free end becomes swollen and finally burst out to discharge their secretions.

D. Simple columnar ciliated epithelium :

Fig. 2.4 Simple columnar ciliated epithelium.

When the simple columnar epithelial cells have hair like processes (cilia) on their free surface, called columnar ciliated epithelium. Each cilium is attached to a particle present in the cytoplasm of the cell close to the free border. These particles are called **basal particles**. This epithelium is found in the fallopian tube, trachea, vasa efferentia, ependyma, etc. Sometimes the cells may be of low columnar or cuboidal type. These cilia help transportation of materials.

E. Glandular epithelium :

The alveoli of many of the glands, such as thyroid follicles, salivary glands, sweat glands, mammary glands, etc. are lined by usually a single layer of cuboidal or low columnar cells. Ducts of some of these glands are also lined by similar epithelial tissue. These are known as glandular epithelium. These are mostly secretory cells of those glands.

Classification of exocrine glands (with ducts)

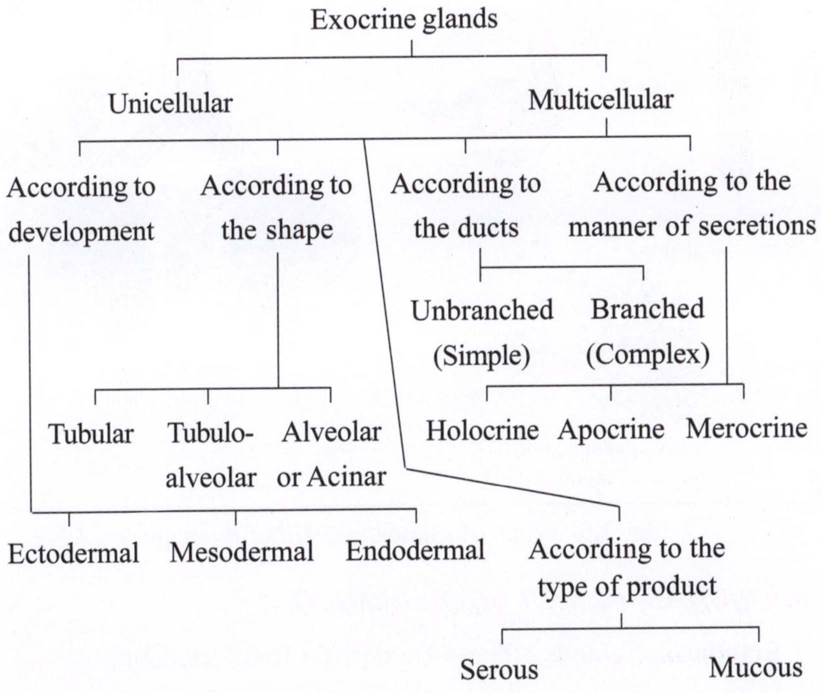

ACCORDING TO THE SHAPE

Tubular glands :

These glands may be in the form of a simple straight tube, example : intestinal glands or coiled tube, example : sweat gland.

Tubulo alveolar gland :

A combination of both tubular and alveolar glands is known as tubulo-alveolar gland.

Example : Salivary gland

Alveolar or Acinous gland :

When the end piece (secretory part) is flask shaped, called alveolar gland and when the end piece is oval or rounded in shape called acinous gland. However, both type of glands are called acinous glands.

Example : Pancreas (exocrine part)

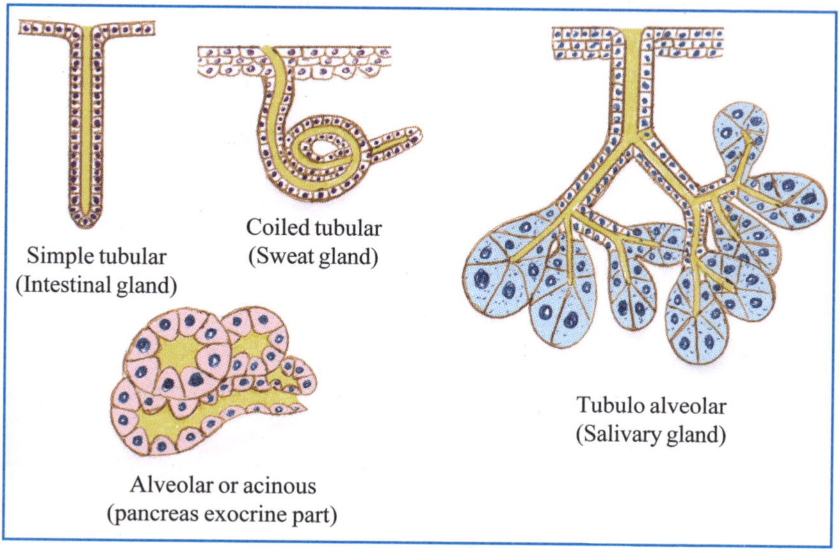

Fig. 2.5 Types of glands according to shape.

ACCORDING TO THE DEVELOPMENT

Ectodermal glands : These are derived from ectoderm.

Example : mammary gland, salivary gland etc.

Mesodermal glands : They are derived from mesoderm.

Example : Adernal cortex, gonads etc.

Endodermal glands : All these glands are derived from endoderm.

Example : Liver, Pancreas, Prostate, Thyroid, Parathyroid etc.

ACCORDING TO THE DUCTS

Unbranched gland : This is the simplest form of gland and the secretion in convayed to the surface by unbranched duct.

Example : Intestinal glands.

Branched gland : When the duct in branched and elaborate, it is known as branched or compound gland.

Example : Salivary gland, Liver, etc.

ACCORDING TO THE MANNER OF SECRETION

Holocrine gland : When the whole body of the cell or cells disintegrate to produce the secretion.

Example : Sebaceous gland.

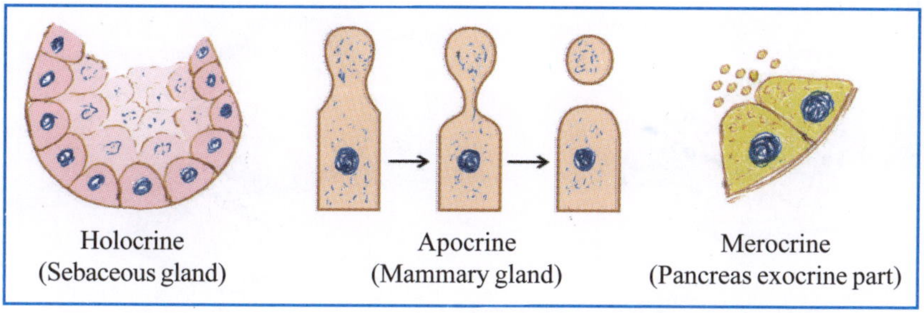

Fig. 2.6 Types of glands according to the manner of secretion.

Apocrine gland : A part of the cells particularly the apex or luminal parts degenerate to form secretory product. The remaining basal portion and the nucleus take part in regeneration of the cell.

Example : mammary gland

Merocrine gland : In the type of gland the secretory product is released in the form of small vesicles without damaging the cell membrane.

Example : Pancreas (exocrine) and most of the other glands.

ACCORDING TO THE TYPE OF PRODUCT

Serous glands : The secretory product is almost a clear fluid. The cytoplasm is generally homogenous.

Example : Parotid salivary gland.

Mucous glands : These glands produce viscous fluid. The cytoplasm appears foamy.

Example : Submandibular salivary gland.

However serous cells are also present in this gland.

Classification of endocrine glands (duct less)

These glands may be classified according to the arrangement of cells.

a) **Cord or clump type**

In these glands the cells are arranged in irregular cords or in clusters. The secretory products of the cells are directly delivered to the surrounding capillaries.

Example : Pituitary, Adrenal

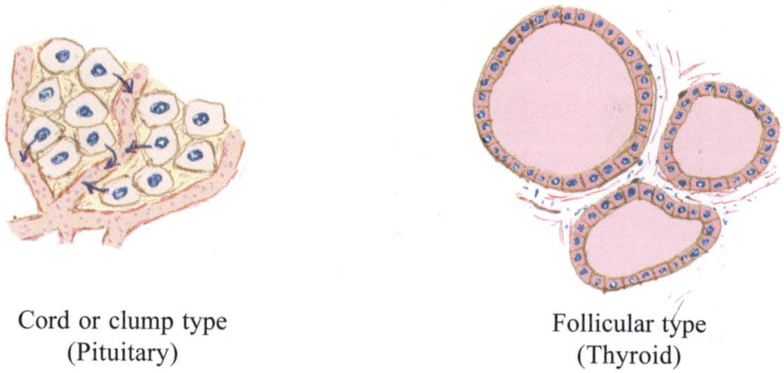

Fig. 2.7 Types of endocrine glands.

b) **Follicular type**

Here the cells are pushed to the periphery and the secretion is stored in the follicle and subsequently delivered to the surrounding capillary.

Example : Thyroid

COMPOUND EPITHELIUM

These epithelial tissues are formed by multiple layers (stratified) of cells arranged on a basement membrane. According to the shape of these cells, the compound epithelium is classified into following types :

A. Stratified squamous epithelium

B. Stratified columnar epithelium

C. Stratified columnar ciliated epithelium

A. Stratified squamous epithelium

There are two types of such epithelium. Stratified squamous cornified and stratified squamous non-cornified.

Stratified squamous cornified epithelium is present in such places where wear and tear is more and is exposed to atmosphere and friction. It is made up of multiple layers of cells and the superficial layer is covered by keratinized material. Epidermis is formed by this type of epithelium. Below the keratinized layer there remain few layers of flattened cells. However in the deeper layer the cells are polyhedral and in further deep layer they are columnar in shape. In this epithelium the surface cells (flat cells) die due to dehydration and lack of nutrition and subsequently become keratinized. Nails are modified stratified squamous cornified epithelium.

Fig. 2.8 Stratified squamous cornified.

Stratified squamous non-cornified epithelium is having similar histological characters to that of cornified but the keratinized layer is absent. This epithelium is present in mouth, pharynx vagina, anal canal, etc. , where wear and tear is more and absorption is less.

Fig. 2.9 Stratified squamous non-cornified.

B. Stratified Columnar epithelium

This epithelium is composed of several layers of columnar and fusiform cells. They are present only in some parts of pharynx, male urethra, fornix of conjunctiva, etc.

C. Stratified columnar ciliated epithelium

Some parts of the laryngeal cavity and nasal surface of the soft palate are lined by multiple layers of columnar cells with cilia on the free surface of the superficial layer.

TRANSITIONAL EPITHELIUM

It is made up of three to four layers of cells – a) Superficial layer of polyhedral cells containing abundant cytoplasm, b) Intermediate pear shaped cells with their bases directed towards the superficial layer and tips directed towards the basement membrane and c) Next one or two layers of cuboidal cells. Transitional epithelium is found in the mucous membrane of urinary bladder, ureter, pelvis of kidneys and parts of urethra and therefore termed uro-epithelium or ***urothelium***. The large superficial cells can withstand stretching of the distended urinary bladder by spreading themselves in a flat manner and are impermeable to fluid.

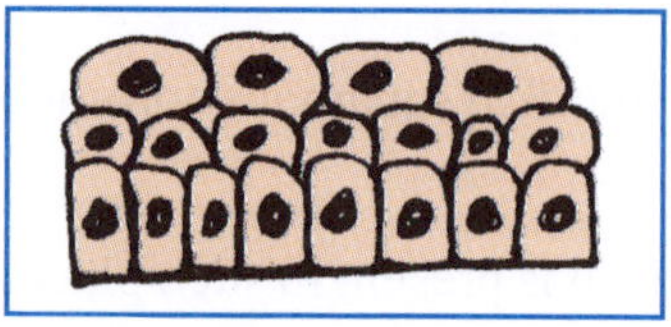

Fig. 2.10 Transitional epithelium.

The shape of the surface cells changes according to the condition of stretching and relaxation and thereby called Transitional. These cells are flexible and yet adhesive to each other.

Epitheloid Cells

In some places some smooth muscle cells are modified to resemble epithelial cells, called epitheloid cells. Example – in the affarent vessels of renal glomerulus, in the arteriovenous anastomosis etc.

Epithelial Metaplasia

When one type of adult normal epithelium is replaced by a different but morphologically still normal adult epithelium, the condition is known as epithelial metaplasia. Example – as a result of chronic irritation from smoking the normal epithelium of bronchus which is citiated psudo-stratified columnar epithelium is changed to stratified squamous epithelium.

CONNECTIVE TISSUE

Tissues under this classification not only connect or bind or support other tissues of the body but perform many other functions. It also forms body fluids. This tissue is derived from mesoderm and composed of two types of substances – Cells and intercellular material.

- Connective Tissue
  - Intercellular substance or matrix
    - Amorphous ground substance
    - Fibers
      - Collagen fibers
      - Elastic fibers
      - Reticular fibers
  - Cells
    - Fibroblasts
    - Macrophases (Histiocytes or Clasmatocytes)
    - Mast cells
    - Plasma cells
    - Fat cells
    - Reticular cells
    - Pigment cells

The **intercellular substance** is composed of an amorphous ground substance and fibrous elements. The matrix is a nonliving material and is synthesized by connective tissue cells.

The **Amorphous ground substance** is mainly composed of water, electrolytes and mucopolysaccharides conjugated with proteins. The ground substance provides a framework of the tissue, helps in binding of cells as well as in the diffusion of metabolites. It acts as mechanical barrier to the cells and helps in preservation of water as tissue fluid. Formation of ground substance may be influenced by hormones. It diminishes with the advancement of age. It can be stained by PAS reagent and metachromically by toluidine blue or by alcian blue.

The **Fibrous elements** are collagen fibers, elastic fibers and reticular fibers. They are mostly derived from fibroblasts.

Collagen Fibers

These are composed of bundles of white fibers. These fibers do not branch and do not run singly but in bundles. These bundles are wavy and run in different directions. These fibers are made up of collagen, a protein and produced by fibroblasts. Within the fibroblasts polypeptide chains are formed from amino acids including praline and lysine. They are hydroxylated to form protocollagen with the help of Vitamin C. Three (3) protocollagen chains unite to form triple helix tropocollagen molecule with the help of glycoproteins. These molecules are released by fobroblasts into the intercellular space and become polymerized to form collagen fibrils. These fibers stain **pink** with eosin, **red** in Van Gieson's stain and **blue** in Mallory's stain.

Elastic Fibers

These are also fibrous tissue and derived from fibroblasts and are little thicker. They are arranged singly or in small bundles but individual fibers may branch to form network. These fibers stretch and recoil easily. Some fibers may be yellowish in colour. They are found in various ligaments – Ligamentum nuchae, Ligamentum flava, in the wall of bronchi, in the wall of arteries, etc. They are composed of a protein-tropo-elastin. They are resistant to chemical treatment. These fibers may be stained with Weigert's resorchin fuchsin and with Verhoeff's stain.

Reticular Fibers

They are generally found in the reticular connective tissue particularly in association with the basement membrane. These are young collagen fibers and form a mesh work on which the cells of the organs rest. They branch and frequently anastomose with each other. The interspaces are small and are largely occupied by lymph and tissue fluid. The reticular fibers are found in the lymph nodes, liver, spleen, bone marrow and in many other organs. They are stained with silver nitrate and PAS method.

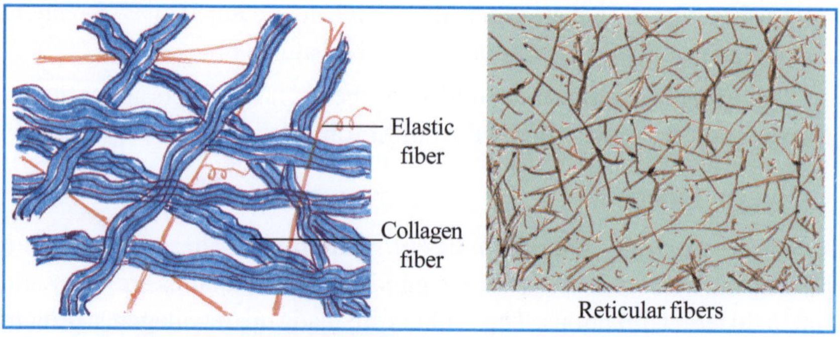

Fig. 2.11 Collagen, Elastic and Reticular fibers.

CELLS OF CONNECTIVE TISSUE

Fibroblasts

These are young fibrocytes and are very active. These cells are fusiform or elongated in shape having numerous processes. Each cell contains an oval centrally placed nucleus. The cytoplasm is basophilic and contains rough surfaced ER, Golgi apparatus and Mitochondria. Old fibroblasts are called fibrocytes. They are inactive, elongated in shape and contain hyperchromatic nuclei. Fibroblasts help in the formation of collagen fibers by synthesizing tropocollagen protein. They also secrete mucopolysaccharide, reticulin and elastin. They help healing of wounds by continuous proliferation. They act as stem cells for other cellular components of connective tissue.

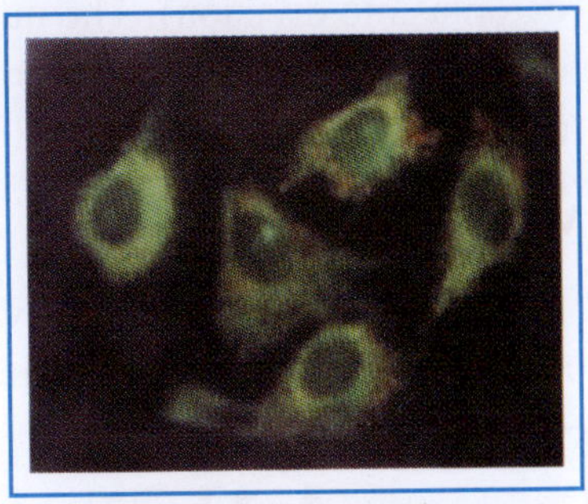

Fig. 2.12 Fibroblasts.

Macrophages (Histiocytes or clasmatocytes)

They are large irregular cells containing one or more nuclei. They have long and short processes which may be sometimes branched. The cytoplasm is basophilic. These cells belong to RE system. Active cells assume outline and move freely. The cells at rest are fixed to reticular fibers. These cells are phagocytic in nature and engulf foreign substances and therefore called big eaters or macrophases. They play role in antigen antibody reaction. They are found in connective tissue as ***histeocytes***, in blood as ***monocytes***, in liver as ***Kupffer's cells***, in lung as ***alveolar phagocytes***, in lymphoid tissue as ***reticular cells*** and in CNS as ***microglia***. They are stained with acidphosphatase (Lysosomal stain) and Aryl sulphate.

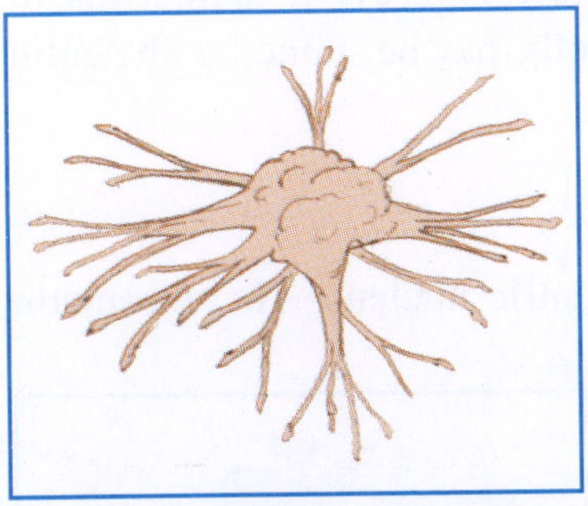

Fig. 2.13 Macrophage.

Langerhans' Giant Cells

When the debris is too large to be phagocytized by a single macrophage, then two or more macrophases fuse together and undergo karyokinesis (nuclear division) without subsequent cytokinesis (cytoplasmic division). The nuclei become scattered through the mass of cytoplasm and sometimes arranged in a horse shoe pattern. It is found in tuberculosis lesions.

Mast Cells

These are large round or oval cells with central nucleus and course intracytoplasmic granules. They are present in the fibrous capsules of liver and other organs, along the blood vessels and in synovial membrane. These cells produce heparin, histamine and small amount of serotonin. They also help in the formation of hyaluronic acid in the matrix. Occasionally the cytophelic antibodies (Ig E) are absorbed on the surface of these Mast cells. When specific antigen enters into the body an antigen-antibody reaction takes place on the surface of these Mast cells and histamine liberates. This event then leads to anaphylactic or allergic reaction. Mast cells may be stained with Anilin dyes.

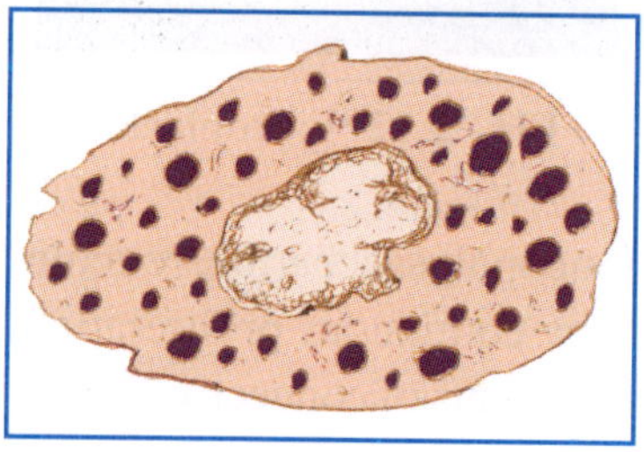

Fig. 2.14 Mast cell.

Plasma Cells

These are large oval cells with eccentric nucleus. The chromatin materials of the nucleus give a cart wheel appearance. They are found in the lymphoid tissue and in the greater omentum. The cytoplasm contains plenty of granular Endoplasmic Reticulum. The B-lymphocytes which are derived from the bone marrow through different lymphoid tissue, differentiate into plasma cells when

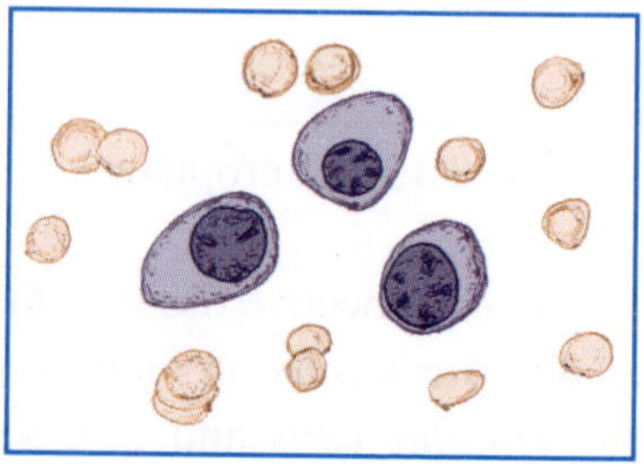

Fig. 2.15 Plasma cells (Blue).

exposed to specific antigen. The cytoplasm contains a Golgi comoplex which appear as an empty space in one side of cytoplasm under light microscope. Plasm cells liberate humoral antibody (IgG) and help in the defence mechanism of the body. These cells can be stained by basic dyes.

Fat Cells

These are fat containing large rounded or polyhedral cells found in the adipose tissue. Due to presence of large number of fat granules, the cytoplasm is pushed peripherally and the nucleus is pushed to one side. Therefore it looks like a signet ring in H&E stained slides as the fat globules appear to be an empty space. The average diameter of fat cells is about 50 microns.

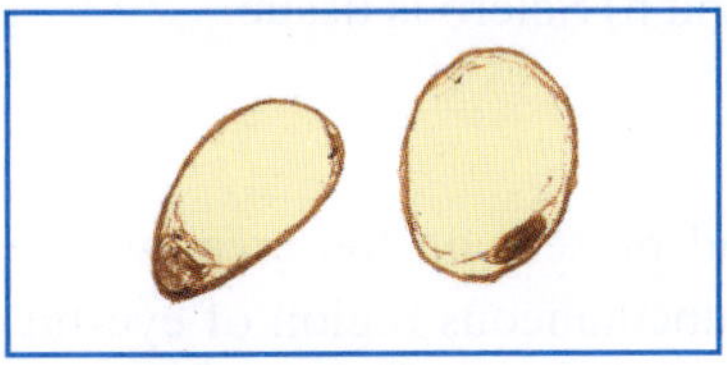

Fig. 2.16 Fat cells.

Reticular Cells

In some glands fine network of reticulin fibers are produced by some branched flattened cells, called Reticular cells. It is difficult to differentiate these cells from fibroblasts. These cells are phagocytic in nature and act as stem cells for the cellular constituent of blood.

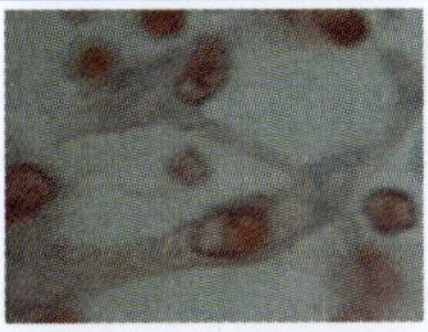

Fig. 2.17 Reticular cells.

Pigment Cells

Pigment containing cells are called Pigment cells. These cytoplasmic pigments are responsible for formation of colour. The pigment is called melanin and the cells are called ***melanocytes***. These cells are found in the skin. In some lower vertebrates the pigment cells are yellow in colour. These pigments generally remain around the nucleus. But due to change

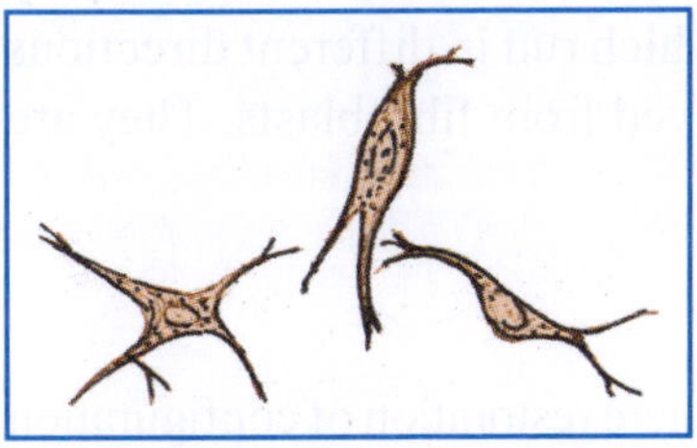

Fig. 2.18 Pigment cells.

of environment these pigments may disperse in the cytoplasm and therefore may lead to change in body colour. Melanocytes are generally stellate shaped cells with long processes and are derived from neural crest cells.

CLASSIFICATION OF CONNECTIVE TISSUE

On the basis of functional importance the connective tissues may collectively classified into a) Areolar tissue, b) Adipose tissue, c) White fibrous tissue, d) Yellow elastic tissue, e) Reticular tissue, f) Mucoid tissue, g) Blood and hemopoetic tissue and h) Sclerous tissue.

AREOLAR TISSUE

This is a loose connective tissue and present on the areas where mobility is required. It is found in the subcutaneous region of eye-lid, penis, submucous coat of alimentary canal, in the subserous zone and within the wall of viscera. It is composed of ***white collagen fibers***, ***yellow elastic fibers***, ***reticular fibers*** and various types of cells such as ***Fibroblasts***, ***Histeocytes***, ***Plasma cells***, etc.

ADIPOSE TISSUE

It is situated in the zone where fat is deposited for the purpose of giving shape of the body parts like limbs, for positioning of some organs and viscera and for storing energy in the form of mesenteric or omental fat. It is composed of ***fat cells***, which contain free fat inside, ***supported by loose framework of areolar tissue***.

WHITE FIBROUS TISSUE

It is present in the region where tensile strength is needed. This tissue is found in the ligaments, tendons and in sheaths. It is formed mainly by wavy bundles of ***white collagen fibers*** which run in different directions without branching. These fibers are derived from fibroblasts. They are present in ligaments, tendons fascia, etc.

YELLOW ELASTIC TISSUE

This tissue is found in hollow viscera where restoration of configuration is required. They are also found in some ligaments. They are yellowish in colour. The fibers are thinner than collagen fibers. The fibers branch and re-join freely, e.g. elastic lamina of aortic wall, ligamenta flava, etc.

RETICULAR TISSUE

Already mentioned.

MUCOID TISSUE

These are semisolid substances and composed of abundant matrix and few cells with branching processes. They are found in the umbilical cord as ***Wharton's jelly***, in the eye ball as ***vitreous body***, in the developing tooth as ***pulp***, etc.

BLOOD AND HEMOPOETIC TISSUE

These are of two types – a) Myeloid tissue and b) Lymphatic tissue.

The Myeloid tissue produces RBC, granular WBC and platelets. These cells are phagocytic in nature.

Lymphatic tissue produces lymphocytes. This tissue may be i) noncapsulated or ii) capsulated. The lymphatic tissue in the form of aggregations within loose connective tissue, such as Pyer's patches are the examples of noncapsulated lymphatic tissue. Lymph nodes, thymus, spleen, lymph glands, tonsils etc. are the capsulated lymphatic tissue.

SCLEROUS TISSUE

Described separately.

SCLEROUS TISSUE

This is a specialized connective tissue and responsible for formation of general framework of the body as well as of some viscera to support soft structures. It is of two types – (i) Cartilage and (ii) Bone.

CARTILAGE

This is a semi hard substance which has a high tensile strength, rigidity, elasticity and resistance to compressive force. It has low vascularity and capacity for growth. Cartilage tissue is present on the articular surfaces of the long bones, walls of the thorax, in the larynx, trachea, bronchi, ear, nose, intra-articular discs, etc. The cartilage which is replaced by bones are known as temporary cartilage. The tissue is composed of abundant intercellular substance or matrix and less quantity of cells. The **Matrix** is composed an amorphous ground substance, made up of water, proteoglycans, lipids and collagenous fibers.

Cartilage cells – The young cells are small and irregular in shape. These cells are more active and are called Chondroblasts. The mature cells are large and more or less rounded in appearance. They are called Chondrocytes. These cells occupy small empty spaces within the ground substance called lacunae.

According to the number of cells and the characteristics of the ground substance the cartilage is classified into a) Hyaline cartilage, b)White fibro -cartilage and c) Yellow elastic cartilage.

Hyaline Cartilage – This cartilage looks like translucent glass and composed of cells and clear ground substance. The ground substance consists mostly of chondrotin sulphate and a few collagen fibers. Most of the cartilages of the body such as articular cartilages, costal cartilages, laryngeal cartilages (except epiglottis), tracheal and bronchial cartilages belong to this group. Excepting articular cartilages, all hyaline cartilages are covered by a fibrous membrane known as perichondrium. The cells are generally arranged in groups of 2, 4, etc. These cells are formed by multiplication of a single parent cell and are therefore found in close association. These cell groups are called cell nests. These cells are large with large nucleus and glycogen rich cytoplasm.

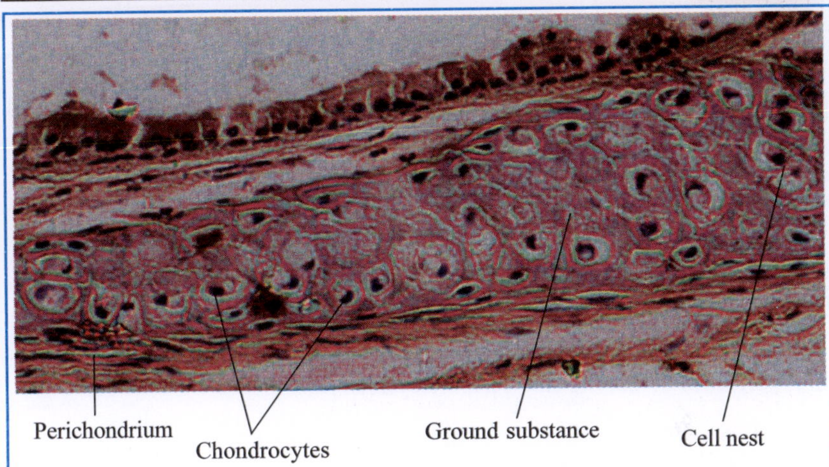

Fig. 2.19 Hyaline cartilage.

1. Chondrocytes – mostly arranged in pairs ;
2. Perichondrium is prominent ;
3. Ground substance – abundant ;
4. Few cell nests are also present.

Articular hyaline cartilage covers the articulating ends of bones in the diarthrodial joints and provides smooth surface to create a wear resistant and friction free environment. This cartilage derives its nutrition from the synovial fluid by which its surface is bathed and from the vessels of synovial membrane and hypochondrium. The cells are generally arranged in four zones. The superficial cells (zone-I) are small ovoid or elongated and are arranged parallel to the surface. The intermediate

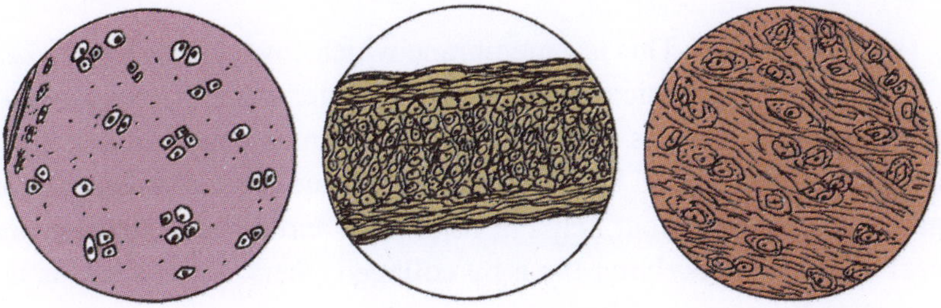

Fig. 2.20 Types of cartilages.

cells (zone-II) are large round and most active. In the next layer (zone-III) large round cells are arranged in a radiating manner, perpendicular to the surface. In the deep layer (zone-IV) the cartilage cells die and bone formation starts.

White fibro-cartilage – This cartilage is composed of bundles of white fibrous tissue in the matrix and scattered groups of cartilage cells. These cells are oval or round in shape and remain surrounded by fibers. These cartilages are present in the areas where maximum tensile strength, flexibility as well as rigidity is necessary. They are found in the intervertebral discs, menisci, pelvic symphysis, etc.

Yellow elastic cartilage – The matrix of this cartilage is composed of amorphous intercellular ground substance which is traversed by yellow elastic fibers and typical chondrocytes. These fibers branch and anastomose with each other. It provides elasticity and at the same time rigidity to maintain shape of certain organs. They are present in the pinna and in some laryngeal cartilages.

BONE

Bones are specialized hard connective tissue, made up of the followings :

(a) Periosteum

(b) Articular cartilage

(c) Bone cells

(d) Inter cellular substance

(e) Bone marrow

(a) ***Perisoteum*** – This is a membrane which covers the outer surface of the bone except articular surfaces. It's outer layer is composed of fibers and blood vessels and the inner layer contains osteoblasts which help in ossification and hence called osteogenic layer. Periosteum not only covers the bone but helps in its growth and repair. Periosteum is attached to the underlying bone by collagen fibers. Periosteum is not present on the sesamoid bones.

(b) ***Articular cartilage*** – These cartilages cover the articular ends of the bones to provide friction-free smooth surface. They are made up of hyaline cartilage. The cells of these cartilage are almost round or elongated and are arranged singly or in groups of even number of cells. These are presumed to be the offsprings of common parent cells.

(c) ***Bone cells*** – These are i) osteoblasts, ii) osteoclasts and iii) osteocytes.

i) **osteoblasts** are bone forming round or oval cells with processes and large nucleus. The cytoplasm is basophilic and contains large number of rER. The cytoplasm is rich in Alkaline phosphatase and helps in mineralization of bone matrix. These are very active cells and produce collagen fibers and organic materials.

ii) **osteoclasts** are large multinucleated cells with pale foamy eosinophilic cytoplasm which is rich in Acid-phosphatase. These cells do not have processes but are provided with branched borders. Osteoclasts are derived from mesenchymal cells like osteoblasts or formed by the fusion of few osteoblasts. They re-absorb bone salts and are active during growth and re-modelling.

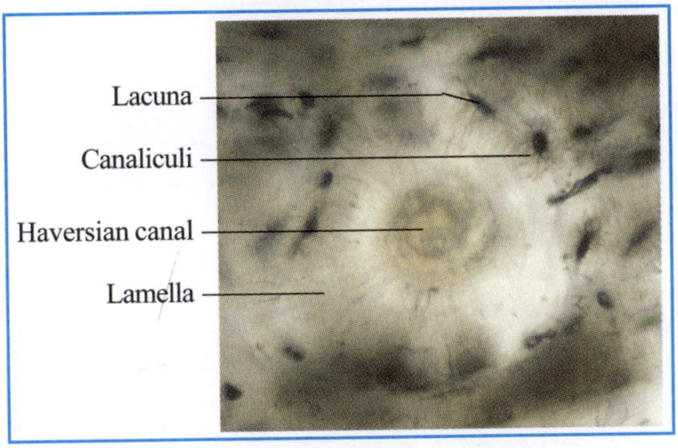

Fig. 2.21 Haversian system.

iii) **osteocytes** are the mature bone cells and are derived from osteoblasts. Each of these cells are housed within tiny spaces surrounded by matrix known as lacunae. These are flattened cells with numerous processes and centrally placed nucleus. The processes are accommodated within the minute canals which extend from the lacunae called canaliculi.

(d) ***Intercellular substance*** – The intercellular ground substance comprises of organic materials and inorganic bone salts. The organic materials are mainly protein polysaccharide complex and collagen fibers embedded in calcified matrix. Inorganic materials are calcium phosphate, calcium carbonate, magnesium phosphate, sodium carbonate, etc.

(e) ***Bone Marrow*** – This is a soft, pulpy and vascular tissue accommodated in the medullary cavity of long bone, and in the marrow spaces of the spongy bones. There are two types of bone marrow – Red and Yellow.

i) Red marrow contains blood cells at their different stages of development, interlacing network of reticular connective tissues, fat cells, lymphoid cells, blood vessels and occasionally megakaryocytes.

ii) Yellow marrow contains connective tissue, blood vessels, fat cells and few mature and immature blood cells.

In infants bone marrow is generally red. With the advancement of age red bone marrow gradually replaced by yellow marrow.

Types of bone tissue

There are two types of bone – compact and spongy.

1. Compact bone

It forms the wall of long cylindrical bones. There is a definite pattern of arrangement in the compact bone called **Osteones** or **Haversian System**. This system comprises of the following :

Haversian canals

These are paralally arranged small canals along the long axis of the bone and are situated at the center of the Haversian system. They accommodate blood vessels, nerves and lymphatics. These parallel canals are communicated by side, branches. They communicate with marrow cavity as well as with surroundings through transverse **canals of Volkmann**.

Lamelle

They are bony layers concentrically arranged around the Haversian canals. These are made up of fine collagen bundles in calcified matrix. The number of these concentric lamellae generally varies from 5 to 10.

At the superficial portion and along the circumference of the long bones few lamellae run parallel to the surface. These outer lamellae are called circumferential lamellae. In between the Haversian systems

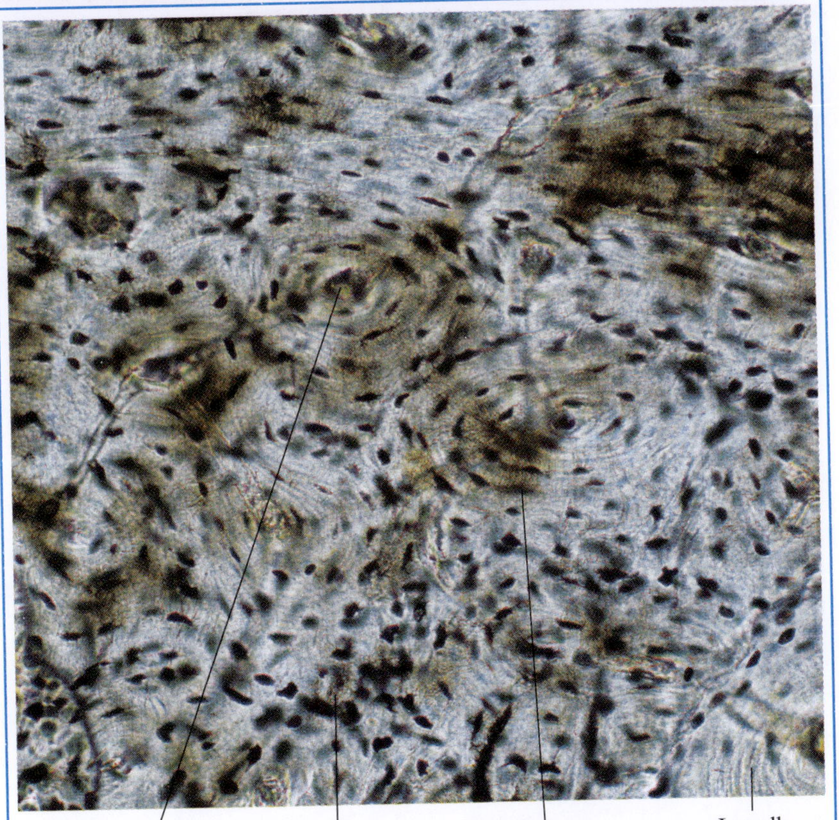

Fig. 2.22 Section of compact bone showing Haversian system.

1. Haversian canal is prominent ;
2. Concentric lamellae are clear ;
3. Lacunae accomodate body of the osteocytes ;
4. Canaliculi house processes of osteocytes.

some irregular bony deposits are found. These are called interstitial lamellae.

Lacunae

These are spaces between these lamellae where osteocytes are housed. From these lacunar spaces very fine canals extend all around in a radiating manner which accommodate fine cytoplasmic processes of the osteocytes. These are known as **canaliculi**. Neighboring lacunae communicate through these canaliculi with each other and also with periosteal tissue spaces.

2. Spongy bone

The substance of all the bones other than shaft of long bones are composed of spongy bone. It looks like hard sponge and contains numerous small spaces between the bony trabeculae and spicules and therefore also called cancellous bone. These minute spaces between the irregular bony plates remain filled up by bone marrow. However the periphery these trabeculae merge with a thin layer of compact bone. The boney trabeculae or the spicules are arranged in such a manner that no osteone is formed.

Although the spongy substance appears to be an irregular network, there is some difinite pattern of placement of the bony plates along the line of force which is to be exerted by the bone in living condition.

MUSCULAR TISSUE

This is a specialized tissue having the property of contractility and designed for movements of an organ or the body. Excepting few, most of the muscles are derived from mesoderm. Only some small muscles, such as arrector pilorum, muscles of iris are ectodermal in origin. Three types of muscles are available in the body as follows :

(I) Skeletal muscle,

(II) Visceral muscle and

(III) Cardiac muscle.

SKELETAL MUSCLE

These muscles are attached to the bones and therefore named skeletal. They are voluntary in nature and striated in appearance under microscope and therefore also called striated muscle.

Composition

A number of fine myofibrils are enclosed in a connective tissue sheath outside the sarcolemma called endomysium and form a ***muscle fiber***. Many muscle fibers are enclosed by another connective tissue membrane or septa known as perimysium and form a muscle bundle or ***fasciculus***. A good number of fasciculi are covered outside by a connective tissue coat called epimysium and a ***muscle*** is formed. The muscle fibers are considered to be units of muscle.

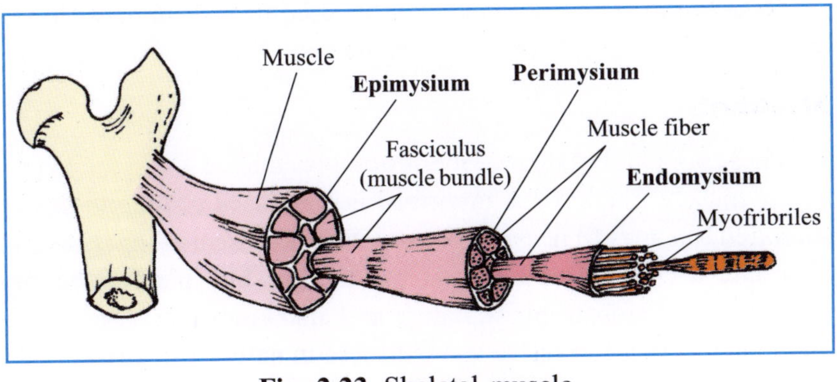

Fig. 2.23 Skeletal muscle.

Structure

A muscle fiber is composed of elongated tubular cells with multiple nuclei and extends along the length of the muscle. A fiber may be 1 to 40 mm in length and 10 micron to 100 micron in breadth.

Sarcolemma

The outer transparent cell membrane of the muscle fiber, having a thickness of about 75Å is called **Sarcolemma**. Like other cell membrane it is composed of outer and inner protein layers and an intermediate lipid layer. The sarcolemma maintains a higher concertration Na^+ and Cl^- outside and a higher concentration of K^+ inside which results a potential difference of about -70 millivolts between them. With the arrival of a nerve impulse at the motor end plate the potential difference abolishes (i.e. depolarization occurs) and the muscle fiber contracts. Inside sercolemma elongated myofibrils, multiple nuclei, mitochondria, a small golgi apparatus are embedded in the sarcoplasm.

Sarcoplasm

It is the samifluid non cotractile cytoplasm of the muscle cell where other constituents of the cell are embedded.

Nuclei – Numerous elongated nuclei are found beneath the sarcolemma. Several hundred nuclei may be present in a single muscle fiber.

Mitochondria or sarcosomes are situated in rows in between the myofibrils and provide energy to the muscle.

Myofibrils

These are parallel thread like structures situated along the length of the muscle fibers. Each myofibril is composed of longitudinally arranged fine **myofilaments**. The myofibrils present along its length alternate dark band and a light band. This dark band is doubly refractive and anisotropic in nature and also known as A band. The light band is non-refractive and isotropic in nature and also called I band.

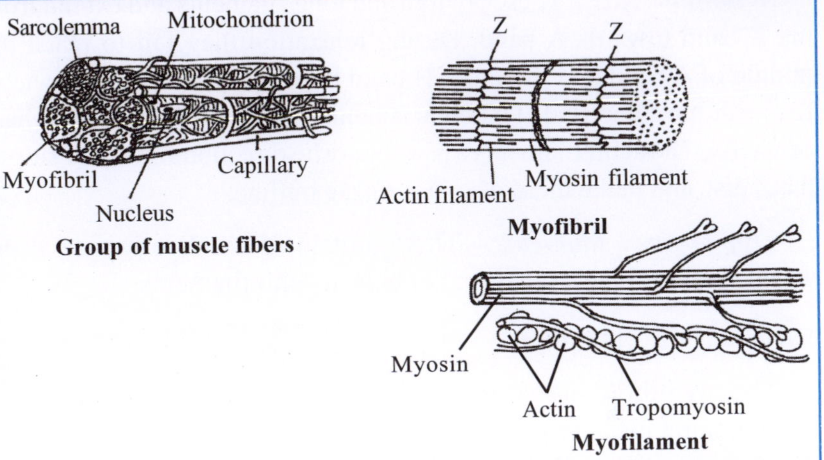

Fig. 2.24 Structure of skeletal muscle fibres under electron microscope.

These A band and I band of adjacent myofibrils are aligned transversely and give a muscle fiber a cross striated appearance. At the middle of the I band, a thin dark transverse line is present. This is known as Z line or Z disc. The portion of the myofibril in between two adjacent z discs is known as **sarcomere**. The sarcomeres are considered to be the contractile unit of a myofibril. Each sarcomere is about 2.5 micron long in a muscle at rest. The A band is bisected at the middle by a lighter zone known as H band. Within the H band a narrow dark line is seen called M band.

Myofilaments

These are fine thread like protein filaments, arranged longitudinally within the myofibrils. They are of three varieties– Myosin, Actin and Tropomyosin.

Myosin filaments – They are thicker and situated longitudinally parallel to each other in the dark A band. These filaments become more thick at the middle (M line) during contraction. They are composed of rods of myosin molecules with globular projection at one end and therefore appears as peripheral bids on the surface on EM.

The rod portion is called light meromyosin and the globular head portionis called heavy meromyosin. These myosin heads link with the actin filaments during contraction.

Actin filaments – These are thin and long filaments and extend from the Z band towards A band. During relaxation they fail to reach the middle of A band and therefore H band becomes prominent. The actin filaments are composed of globular subunits of G-actins in a double chain of a helix. The actin filament twist in opposite directions on either side of the Z disc and make the Z disc in a zigzag outline.

Tropomyosin filaments – These protein filaments originate at the groove between the two strands of helical actin filaments.

Sarcoplasmic reticulum

The myofibrils are surrounded by smooth surfaced circular and branching tubules derived as tubular ingrowths from the sarcolemma. These tubules are called sarcoplasmic reticulum. The circular tubules are known as centrotubules and extend around the Z disc and also called T system membrane. These tubules play a role of conveying the waves of depolarization from the saecolemma to every sarcomere.

VISCERAL MUSCLES

These muscles form the wall of hollow visceral organs, ducts, glands, blood vessels, etc. and therefore called visceral muscles. They are involuntary in nature. These muscle fibers are not transversely striated and for this reason they are also called ***smooth muscle***.

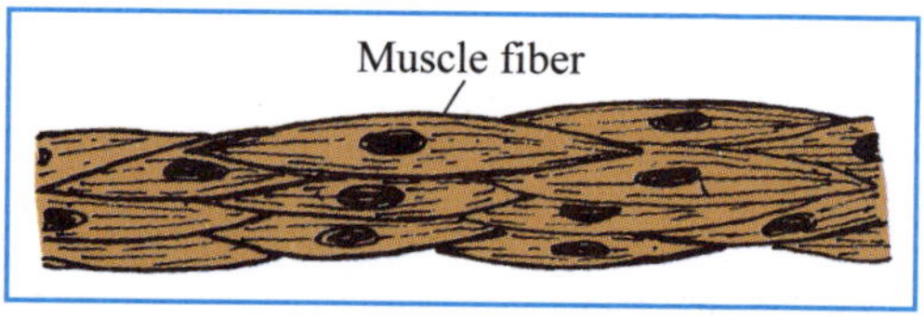

Fig. 2.25 Smooth muscle.

Composition – This muscle is composed of numerous spindle shaped muscle fibers of various length and are arranged in a compact manner in sheets or layers. The fibers are hold together by areolar tissue and are organized according to the function of the viscera. They may be longitudinal, circular, spiral or irregular.

Structure – The structure of these muscle fibers are elongated and fusiform. The central portion is wide and the ends are tapering. The average length is about 200 microns and breadth of the central wide portion is about 6 microns. The cytoplasm contains longitudinally arranged myofribils. The nucleus is elongated, oval and centrally placed. The fibers are arranged in such a way, that the thick middle portion remain in contact with the thin portion of the other fibers. Mitochondria are present between myofibrils. The sarcoplasm is homogeneous. No band or cross striations are seen. Actin and myosin filaments are present. Sarcolemma is surrounded by a basement membrane and reticular fibers which join with the reticular fibers of adjacent cells.

CARDIAC MUSCLE

This muscle forms the wall (Myocardium) of heart and roots of large blood vessels attached to the heart. It is involuntary in nature and contracts rhythmically. The fibers exhibit striations.

Composition – The cardiac muscle is composed of numerous specialized types of muscle fibers which bifurcate and come in contact with neighboring fibers and appears falsely as a syncytial structure under light microscope. The cross striations are not prominent in these fibers. The cytoplasm shows a dark transverse line at certain intervals which make the limiting membranes of two adjacent cells called **Intercalated disc**.

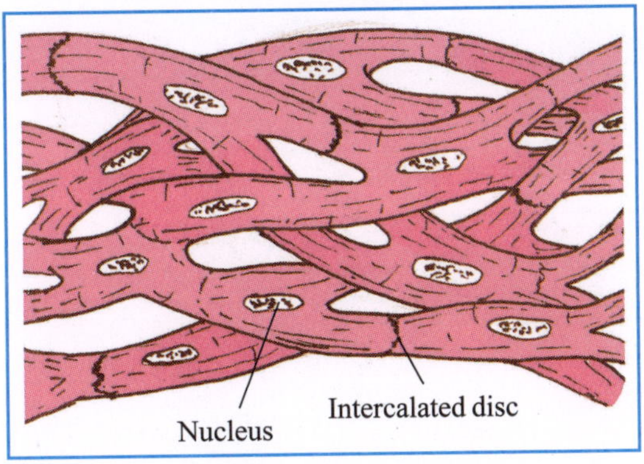

Fig. 2.26 Cardiac muscle.

Structure – These muscle fibers or myocytes are separated from each other by endomysium. Each fiber is about 80 micron in length and 16 micron in breadth. These muscle cells divide into two or more branches and come in contact with neighboring cells. Each cell contains a single centrally placed elongated nucleus. Perimysium is found between the fiber bundles. Mitochondria are more numerous and are arranged in rows in between the myofibrils. Sarcoplasmic reticulum is similar to those of skeletal muscles. T system is present at the level of Z line.

Myoglobin and glycogen are abundant in cardiac muscle. Myofibrils are more or less similar to those of skeletal muscles. The intercalated discs extend across the whole width of the fiber or its branches. The individual muscle cells join end to end by intercalated discs.

NERVOUS TISSUE

The nervous system receives information with regards to the change of environment (external and internal) of the body and in response regulates appropriate function. Therefore the tissue of this system is specialized in nature and complex in structure. Except the microglia the tissue of the system are ectodermal in origin. Microglia develop from mesoderm.

The morphological sub division of this system is as follows : A) Central Nervous System (CNS) – This part comprises of brain and spinal cord and remain covered by bones. B) Peripheral Nervous System (PNS) – This is composed of cranial and spinal nerves and their ganglia. C) Autonomic Nervous System (ANS) – This is the visceral component of the nervous system and composed of autonomic nerves, ganglia and specialized parts of CNS and PNS.

There are two types of basic cells in the nervous tissue. These are Neurons (main cells) and Neuroglia (supporting cells). Some other cells such as ependymal cells of CNS and Schwann cells of P N S are also important constituents of the nervous tissue.

NEURONS

These are the excitable parenchymal cells and are the structural and functional units of the nervous system. A neuron is composed of a cell body or soma and cytoplasmic extensions from the cell. These processeses are of two types- one or more dendrites which convay impulses towards the cell body and a single axon transmits impulses away from the soma.

Cell body or soma

These are present in the grey matter, in various nuclei of CNS and in the ganglia of PNS and ANS. The **size** of the cells varies from 5μ to130μ depending upon their situation. The **shape** of these cells depends on the number of dendrites. The multipolar cells are generally star shaped or pyramid shaped and the unipolar or pseudo-unipolar cells are round in shape. Some bipolar cells are fusiform or flask like in appearance. The Nucleus is mostly central in position. It is large vesicular and contains a

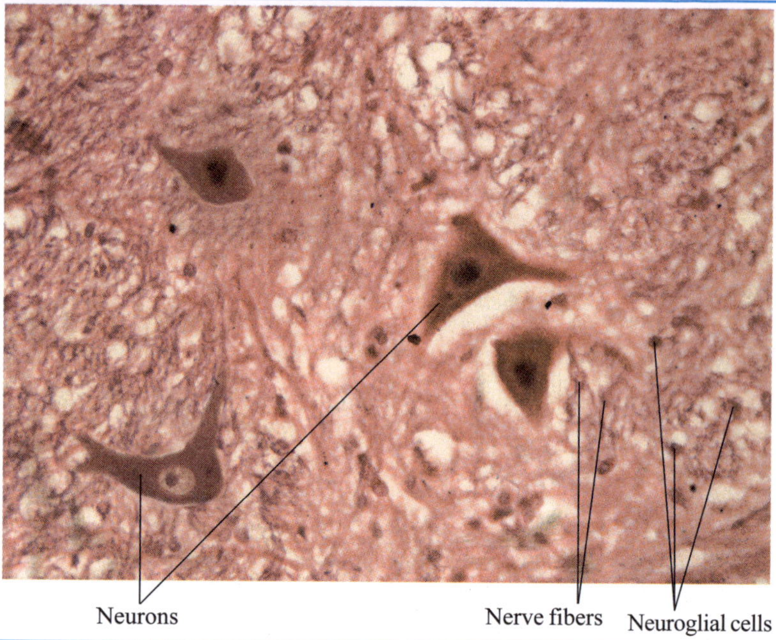

Fig. 2.27 Section of nerve tissue.

1. Triangular or polygonal large bodies of neurons are visible ;
2. Neuroglial cells (small) are plenty ;
3. Nerve fibers have formed meshwork.

prominent nucleolus. However in injury or in the fatigue state of the nerve cells the nucleus may be eccentric in position.

Plasma membrane

It contains integral membrane proteins and functions as ion-selective channels for K, Na, Ca cations and Cl anions. The plasma membrane of the cell body and dendrites contains receptor-protein molecules which become activated by neurotransmitters from other neurons.

The cytoplasm contains the following structures :

Neurofilaments – These are fine thread like cytoplasmic fibrils arranged in a plexiform manner within the cell body and processes. They provide mechanical support to the cell body. These filaments and microtubules crowed together at the axon hillock.

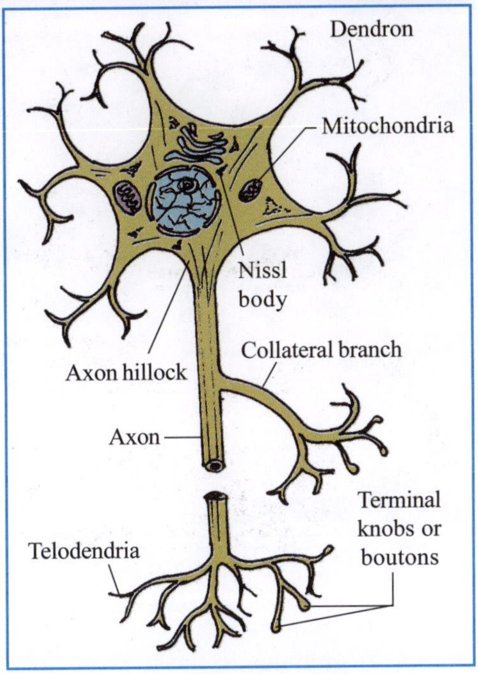

Fig. 2.28 A neurone (diagramatic).

Nissl bodies – These are small triangular structures, present in the cytoplasm of the cell body and dendrites but absent in the axon hillock and axon as they cannot percolate through the crowded neurofibrils. Closely packed ribosome granules in combination with iron become attached to rough surfaced endoplasmic reticulum and form Nissl bodies. These bodies are associated with the synthesis of proteins and enzymes. These bodies degenerate and disappear when the neuron is injured. This is called chromatolysis. They re-appear with the recovery of the neuron.

Mitochondria – These are oval elongated in shape and distributed throughout the cytoplasm of the cell body and processes.

Golgi apparatus – It is placed close to the nucleus in some neurons and helps in storing and releasing neurosecretions.

Lysosomes – These thick walled membranous vesicles with their enzymes hydrolyse Nissl bodies during chromatolysis.

Centrioles – Since the adult neurons do not divide it was believed that there is no centrioles in the nerve cells but its presence has been demonstrated by EM. They probably help regeneration of the cytoplasmic microtubules.

Inclusions – Neuro-melanin, a degradation product of catacolamine, found in the cell bodies of substantia niagra of mid brain. Lipochrome and senility pigments (Lypofuscin) appear as

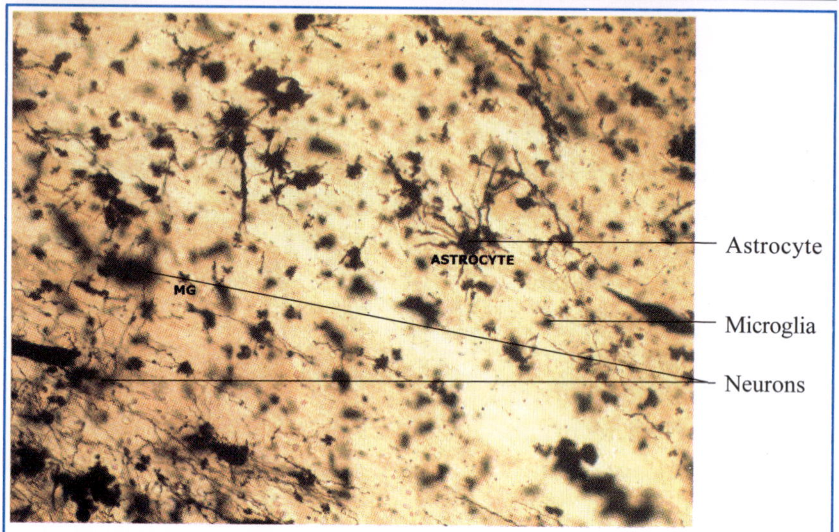

Fig. 2.29 Section of nerve tissue, Golgi cox stain.
(Courtesy : Dr. B. Pal)

clumps of granules in the neurons of old age. Metallic elements like Copper, Zinc and Iron may also be found in some neurons.

Cell processes

Dendrties – These are afferent processes or cytoplasmic extensions of the cell bodies of neurons. They may be single or multiple. They receive and convay nerve impulses towards the cell body. They may branch tremendously. The surfaces of these branches are studded with neumorous projections called spines, which act as contact zones with other neurons. Dendrites of some peripheral nerves have structures similar to those of axons.

Axons – This is the single long process extends from cell body and generally carry nerve impulses away. The point of origin of this process from the cell body is known as ***axon hillock***. Axon forms the structural basis of a nerve fiber. The axon is selender, long tubular structure of almost uniform diameter. The length of an axon may be more than one meter. It remains filled up by a fluid known as ***axoplasm*** which accommodates mitochondria and neurofilaments. The axon remains surrounded by a ***myelin sheath***. The Schwann cells undergo spirelling around the axon and deposit concentric layers of lipid and protein to form myelin sheath. In somatic nerves the myelin sheath is covered by ***neurolemma*** – formed by the body of the Schwann cells. Post ganglionic autonomic fibers have no myelin sheath. The preganglionic autonomic fibers are medulated. In the CNS the myelin sheath is derived from oligodendrocytes. In myelinated nerve collateral branches arise at right angles from the side of the axon at the node of Ranvier. The terminal branches of the axon or its collaterals are known as **Telodendria**. These terminals form bulber swellings at their ends known as **Terminal knobs** or boutons. A special form of termination of axon in a skeletal muscle is known as **motor end plate**. **Node of Ranvier** – At the myelinated nerve fibers, gaps occur at the junction between Schawann cells where the axon cylinder is exposed. These gaps are known as nodes of Ranvier.

Classification of Neurons

According to the number of processes

1. ***Unipolar neurons***

When a nerve cell possesses only one process (axon), it is called unipolar neuron. True unipolar neurons are found only in the mesencephalic nucleus of trigeminal nerve.

The cells of the dorsal root ganglia of spinal nerves and of corresponding ganglia of cranial nerves have single process at the beginning. But it bifurcates into a peripheral part and a central part. The peripheral branches are long and extend to the muscles and skin and are dendritic in function. The central branches enter CNS through dorsal roots and are axonal in

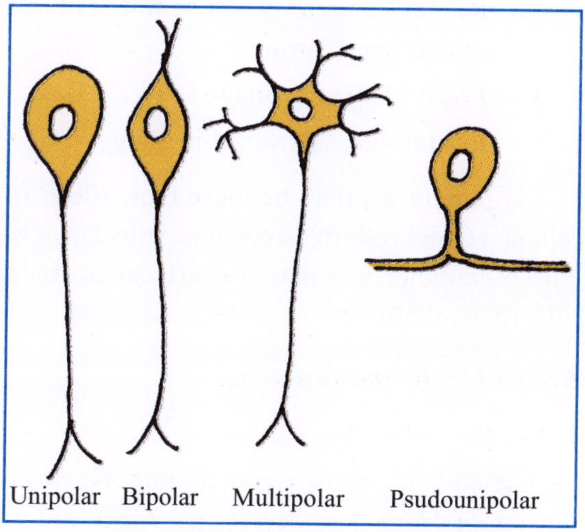

Fig. 2.30 Types of neurons.

function. These neurons are called pseudo-unipolar neurons because developmentally these cells are bipolar and their two poles subsequently united to form a single process.

2. ***Bipolar neurons***

Neurons with two processes are called bipolar neurons. They are generally spindle shaped cells and are found in the spiral ganglion of cochlea, olfactory epithelium and retina.

3. ***Multipolar neurons***

The neurons having more than two processes are called multipolar neurons. Most of the neurons of CNS are multipolar.

According to the length of axon :

Golgi type-I neurons – They have long axons. They may form tracts or pass out of the spinal cord through peripheral nerves. Example – tract cells, ventral horn cells.

Golgi type-II neurons – These cells have short axon. They are generally confined in the CNS, Example – Association neurons.

According to the shape and size of the cells body

1. ***Stellate*** – Star shaped
2. ***Fusiform*** – Spindle shaped
3. ***Basket*** – A neuron whose fibrils of axon surround the cell body of another neuron.
4. ***Flask shaped*** – Shape is like a flask
5. ***Pyramidal*** – Pyramid in shape

Large neurons may be more than 100 μ in diameter; e.g., Purkinje cells and Golgi cells of cerebellum, spinal ganglionic cells etc. The neurons with a diameter less than 7 μ are called micro neurons; e.g., granular cells of cerebellum.

According to the function

1. ***Sensory neurons (afferent)***

The cells are mostly pseudounipolar or biopolar. These cells carry sensations from periphery to the CNS and are situated out side CNS (except mesencephalic nucleus) ; e.g., cells of dorsal root ganglion.

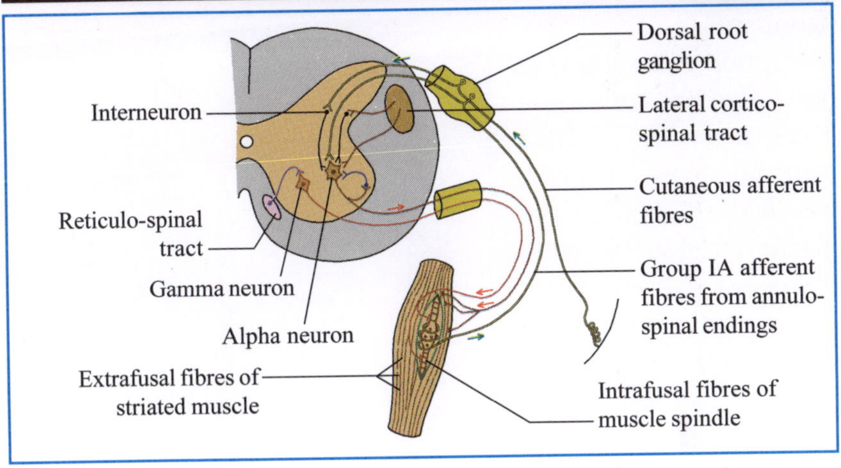

Fig. 2.31 Neurons of the anterior grey column and their functional role.

2. ***Internuncial (connector) neurons***

They are interposed between and connecting two other neurons and also called connector or inter neurons. They are generally multipolar and remain confined within the grey matter of spinal cord or brain.

3. ***Motor neurons (efferent)***

These are multipolar cells and are mostly situated in the CNS. However, post ganglionic autonomic neurons are situated outside CNS.

The motor neurons of the cerebral cortex and cranial part of brain stem are called ***upper motor neurons*** and those of spinal cord and caudal part of brain stem are called ***lower motor neurons***.

Nuclei and ganglia

A group of neurons situated in a particular area of CNS, is called ***nucleus*** and such group of cells present in a particular structure out side CNS, is called ***ganglion***. However, this rule is not always followed.

Nerve fibers

They are the axons or dendrons of a nerve cells. They are classified on the basis of myelin sheath.

a) **Myelinated (medulated) fibers** – Here the axons are enveloped by myelin or medullary sheath which is composed of lipoprotein complex containing unsaturated fatty acid and formed by many layers of modified cell membrane. It gives the white colour of the nerve. These are found in the peripheral nervers and in the white matter of the CNS. Myelin sheath is derived from the Schwann cells in the peripheral nerves and oligodendrocytes in CNS.

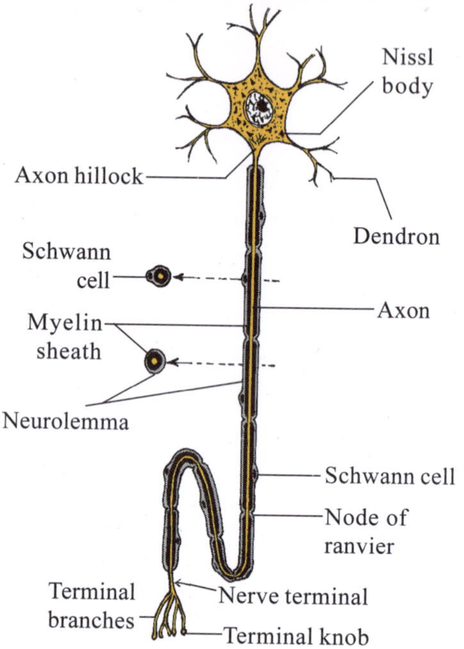

Fig. 2.32 Structure of a neuron.

Nerve trunk : This is a cord or thread like structure made up of bundles of axons out side the CNS. Each axon is covered by a myelin sheath which is again enveloped by connective tissue covering known as ***endoneurium***. A number of such fibers are grouped together and

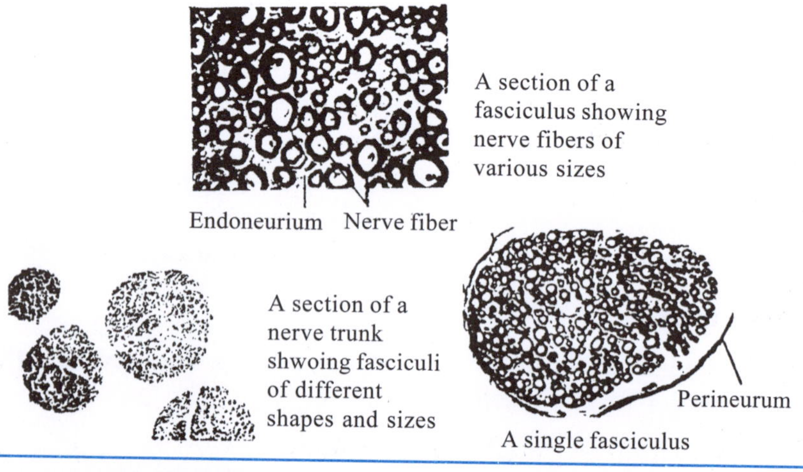

Fig. 2.33 Section of a nerve trunk and its fibers.

covered by a layer called ***perineurium***. Each such group is known as ***Fasciculus***. Numerous fasciculi are bound together and enveloped by a connective tissue sheath known as epineurium. This bundle of fasciculi is the nerve trunk.

b) **Unmyelinated nerve fibers** – They are found in the postganglionic autonomic fibers and in some smaller axons in the CNS. In the PNS the ***fibers are enveloped within simple clefts of Schwann cells*** without any spiraling. The ***nodes of Ranvier are absent***. In the CNS the fibers are not ensheathed and run free among the prosses of other neurons and glial cells.

c) **Naked nerve fibers** – They are found in the grey matter of CNS and in the free nerve endings. They are devoid of myelin sheath and sheath of Schwann cells.

Supporting cells of the nervous system

C N S a) Neuroglia
b) Ependyma

P N S a) Schwann cells
b) Satellite cells

Neuroglia

These supporting cells of CNS are nonconducting elements and form a framework in between the neurons. The sizes of these cells are small and the number of these cells are many times more than the number of neurons. They are of following types :

i) Macroglia – They are moderately large cells and include astrocytes and oligodendrocytes.

Astrocytes – These are star shaped cells with numerous branched processes and contain large round or oval nucleus. They are developed from the embryonic neuroectoderm. The astrocytes with short and thick processes and remain confined in the ***grey*** matter are called **Protoplasmic astrocytes**. Other variety of astrocytes have thin and long processes and remain in the ***white*** matter. These are known as **Fibrous astrocytes**.

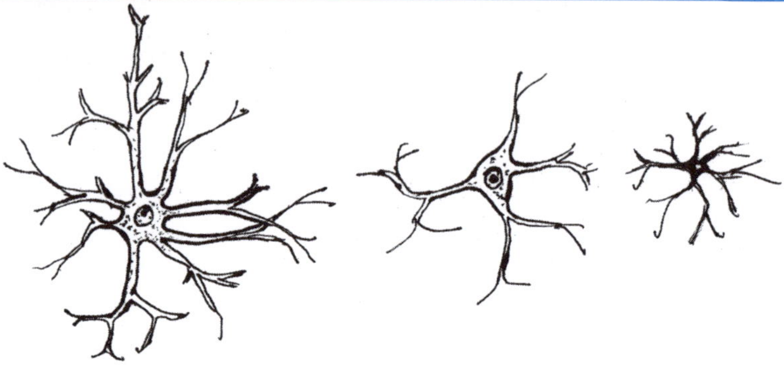

Fig. 2.34 Types of neuroglial cells.

Some processes of astrocytes become attached to the outer surface of the capillaries of the brain and help establishing blood brain barrier. They also provide nutrition in addition to framework support to the nerve tissue.

Oligodendrocytes – They are small cells with few processes and found in both grey and white matter. They form satellite cells in grey matter and peri-fascicular cells in the form of rows in the white matter.

ii) Microglia – These are small cells with thorny projections. They are found more in the grey matter and less in white matter. ***Microglia are derived from mesoderm***. They are the macrophases of CNS.

Ependyma

This is the epithelial lining of the ventricles of the brain and central canal of spinal cord. It is composed of a single layer of low columnar ciliated cells. Some ependymal cells lining the floor of the 3rd ventricle possess long cytoplasmic processes which extend in to the nerve tissue are called **Tanycites**. The ependyma lining the choroid plexus of the ventricles take active part in the formation of CSF. This layer also forms the blood-CSF barrier.

Schwann cells

These are flat cells undergo spiraling around the axons outside the CNS. Each axon comes with the contact of many Schwann cells and form myelin sheath by depositing concentric layers of lipid and protein. The sheath is interrupted at regular intervals in between the covering of the Schwann cells and these exposed parts of axolemma are called nodes of Ranvier. Schwann cells are derived from neural crest cells.

Satellite cells

These are small flat cells derived from neural crest cells and form a capsule around each ganglion cell. Some olegodendrocytes also serve the purpose of satellite cells around the cells of grey matter

Nerve ending – The peripheral nerve fibers whether sensory or motor end in arborization either on some other neurons to form synapse or in the components of some organs like skin, muscle, glands, joint capsule, etc. Close to the termination a nerve fiber loose the neurolemma first, then the myelin sheath.

Synapse

It is the junction, where one neuron ends and another neuron begins. The terminal branches of one axon come in contact with the cell body or dendrites of the next neuron and conduct the impulse in one direction. The terminals of an axon form small swellings called terminal bouton. In synapse, these are closely applied to the dendrites or on the cell bodies of other neurons. The minute gap between the two neurons at the point of contact is called ***synaptic cleft***, which is about 20 nm wide. The chemical substances like acetylcholine, norepinephrine, dopamine, serotonin etc are released from the nerve terminals of presynaptic neuron which flow towards the postsynaptic neuron. These substances are called neurotransmitters. Generally a single type of neurotransmitter is released in the form of secretory vesicle.

According to the locations on the post-synatic neurons, the synapse may be ***Axo-dendritic***, ***Axo-somatic***, ***Axo-axonal*** or ***Dendro-dendritic***.

Motor nerve endings

They terminate in the muscles or glands. The naked axon divides into a number of terminal branches. The small swellings at the end of these terminals knobs contain several mitochondria and vesicles. The sarcolemma of the muscle fiber forms depressions or gutters, where the terminal knobs are inserted. The endoneurium is extended over the nerve terminals to the surface of a muscle fiber and fuse with the endomysium. The neurotransmitter in such nerve endings is acetylcholine.

One muscle fiber receives one terminal knob called **motor end plate**. One axon form several terminal branches and therefore innervate many muscles fibers. All these muscle fibers innervated by the terminals of a single axon is called a ***moter unit***.

One or more terminal knobs of nonmyelinated nerve fibers end on the surface of the plasma membrane of cardiac and smooth muscle fibers. In glands they end among the epithelial cells.

Sensory nerve endings

These are also called receptors. These nerve endings may be naked or encapsulated.

Naked (Free) nerve endings are devoid of any covering and receives pain and tactile (touch) sensations. Touch sensation may also be felt by the hairs indirectly when these free nerve endings become associated with hair follicles.

Encapsulated nerve endings – Here the naked nerve terminals are covered by capsules of connective tissue. There are several varieties of these nerve endings.

a) Pacinian corpuscle – Here the naked terminal is covered by a concentric layers of lamellae and therefore it looks like a knob and receives touch and pressure sensation. They are present in dermis, ligaments, etc.

b) Meissner's corpuscle – This type of capsule is like a irregular cylinder. It receives fine touch sensation and found in the dermis of hands, lips, teat, etc.

Nerve ending in the form of specialized cells

Here actually the nerve endings are attached to some specialized cells who act as receptors. e.g. Rods and cones of retina, Hair cells of organ of Corti.

Some receptor cells in association with surrounding cells form a cell group or sense organ. e.g. Taste bud.

Muscle spindle

This is the sensory organ of skeletal muscle. It is the receptor of stretch reflex and proprioception. Muscle spindles are fusiform structures, comprise of 10 – 12 small modified muscle fibers remain encapsulated by a fibrous sheath. These spindles are situated within the ordinary muscle fibers and their capsules merges with the connective tissue sheath of the adjoining fibers. The ordinary muscle fibers are called **extrafusal** fibers and the muscle fibers remaining within the spindle are called **intrafusal fibers**. There are two types of intrafusal fibers – (a) Neuclear bag fibers and (b) Nuclear chain fibers. In the bag type fibers the nuclei are aggregated in a bag type swollen middle portion and in chain type fibers the nuclei arearranged in a single row. Contractile elements are present only at the ends of these intrafusal fibers. Sensory nerve endings spiral around the mid portion and the motor fibers supply the ends of these intrafusal fibers.

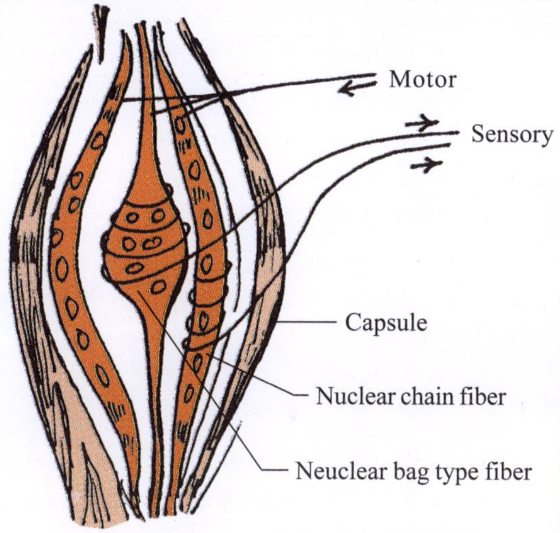

Fig. 2.35 Neuromuscular spindle.

SPINAL CORD

Spinal cord is the solid cylindrical part of CNS situated in the vertebral canal and extends from the level of foramen magnum as the continuation of medulla oblongata to the caudal border of 1st lumbar vertebra.

It is composed of a central grey matter and peripheral white matter. Along the central axis of the spinal cord a canal exists, which extends from the 4th ventricle at the caudal half of the medulla oblongata to the conus medullaris in the form of a minute tube. It contains cerebro spinal fluid during life and is lined by a single layer of ciliated columnar epithelium

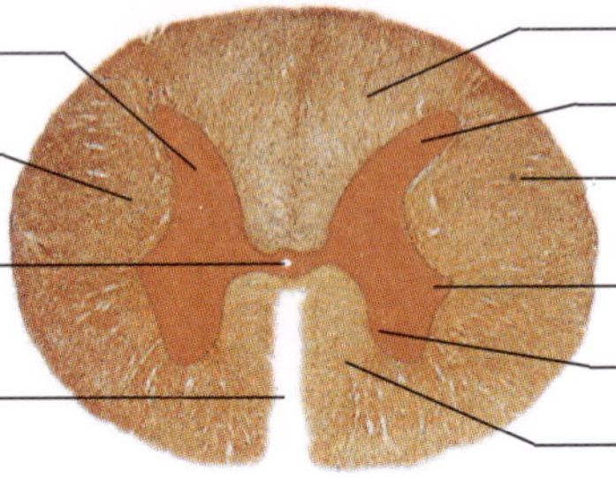

Fig. 2.36 Spinal cord (Transverse section).

1. Grey matter is in the form of the letter 'H' ;
2. Central canal is prominent ;
3. Dorsal, ventral and lateral funiculi of white matter are clear ;
4. Ventral groove is deep.

called **ependyma**. The ependyma is continuous with that of ventricles of the brain.

White matter

This component occupies the spaces at the periphery of the spinal cord and almost surrounds the butterfly shaped central grey matter. It is composed of bundles of nerve fibers, neuroglia and blood vessels. The nerve fibers are mostly thick and myelinated and that is why it is white in appearance. However large number of small calibered and non-myelinated fibers are also present in the white matter. Each half of the white matter is divided into dorsal, lateral and ventral regions, popularly known as funiculi. The white matter consists of ascending tracts of sensory fibers and descending tracts of motor fibers.

The **ventral funiculus** extend from the antero-median fissure to the region of ventral nerve roots. Ventral white commisure connects the ventral funiculi of both the sides and intervenes between the ventral grey commisure and the roof of the ventral median fissure. The **Dorsal funiculus** extends from the postero-median sulcus to the postero-lateral sulcus. Cranial to the mid thoracic region the dorsal funiculus is subdivided into a medial part, the **fasciculus gracialis** and a lateral part, the **fasciculus cuneatus**.

The **Lateral funiculus** is situated in between the dorsal and ventral funiculi and lateral to the grey matter.

Grey matter

It is the centrally placed H or butterfly shaped column of dark or grey substance which extends throughout the length of spinal cord. It is composed of neurons and their processes, neuroglia and blood vessels. Each half of the grey matter comprises of a dorsal horn, a ventral horn and in some specific zone a lateral horn.

Dorsal horn

This is narrow, directed dorsolaterally towards the postero-lateral sulcus. It is separated from the surface by a narrow band called dorso lateral fasiculus. The end of the dorsal horn is capped with translucent mass of nerve tissue, known as ***substintia gelatinosa***. It forms the sensory part of the grey matter and accommodates small multipolar nerve cells. These sensory neurons receives the sensory fibers from the dorsal root ganglion and give rise to second order fibers.

Ventral horn

It is broad, short and directed antero-laterally. It does not extend up to the surface and accommodates large multipolar motor neurons. Axons of these cells form the ventral roots of the spinal nerves.

Lateral horn

It is found at the level of throracic and cranial lumber part of the spinal cord in the form of a lateral projection. It contains the preganglionic sympathetic neurons of autonomic nervous system.

CEREBELLUM

The cerebellar mass is composed of a central core of white matter and peripheral layer of grey matter called cerebellar cortex. Four pairs of cerebellar nuclei are embedded into the white matter of the organ. These are nucleus **Fastigi**, nucleus **Globosus**, nucleus **Emboliformis** and nucleus **Dentate**. The cortex is covered by thin layer of pia mater.

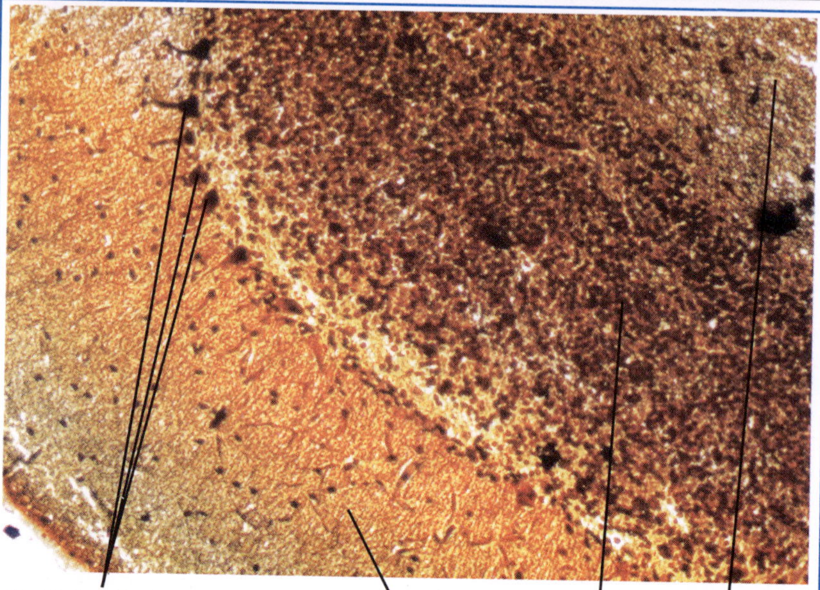

Fig. 2.37 Section of cerebellum.

1. Large flask shaped Purkinje cells are arranged in a single row;
2. Outer molecular layer is thick and clear ;
3. Inner granular layer is dark and contains numerous granule cells.

Cerebellar Cortex

It exhibits an uniform histological organization in all parts of the structure and arranged accordingly as per the depressions and infoldings of the surface. It is composed of three layers of cells.

(a) ***Outer molecular layer*** – It is composed of small molecular cells and two types of neurons – Stellate cells and basket cells. It contains plenty of unmyelinated fibres derived from stellate cells, basket cells, sensory climbing fibers and dendrites of Purkinje cells and Golgi cells.

(b) ***Intermediate Purkinje cell layer*** – This is composed of a single layer of large flask shaped cells called Purkinje cells. The dendrites of

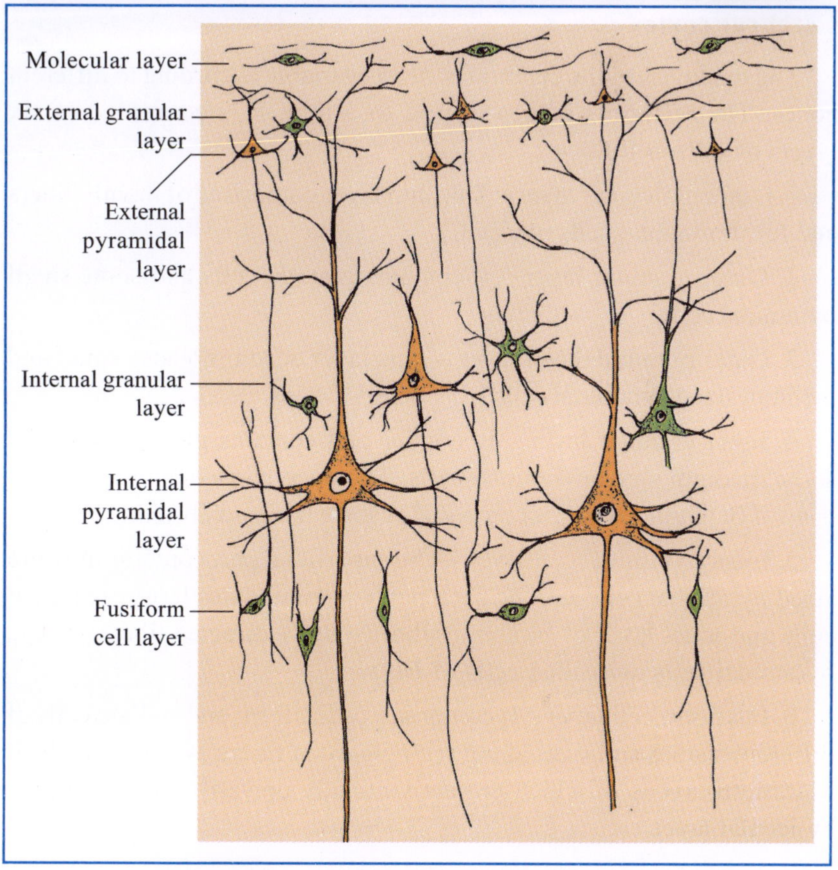

Fig. 2.38 Cerebral cortex (diagramatic).

these cells are in the form of a bush and distributed in the outer molecular layer. Their axons pass downward and synapse with the deep cerebellar nluclei.

(c) ***Inner granular layer*** – It is a thick zone, covers the white matter and composed of closely packed small granule cells. This layer also contain dendrites of Golgi cells and sensory fibers.

CEREBRUM

It comprises of a layer of grey matter called cerebral cortex, which remains covered by pia mater and a central core of white matter. The basal ganglia are embedded within the white matter.

Cerebral cortex

The thickness of the cerebral cortex is variable according to different zones. The thickness ranges from 2 to 5 mm. It is composed of six layers of cells as follows :

1. Outer molecular layer – This thin layer comprises of mainly fibers and few horizontal cells of Cajal.

2. Outer granular layer – It contains granule cells and some small pyramidal cells.

3. Outer pyramidal cell layer – This layer accommodates small and medium sized pyramidal cells.

4. Inner granular layer – It's upper part contains granule cells and some medium sized pyramidal cells. The deep part contains the outer band of Baillarger, which is composed of some horizontally directed fibers.

5. Inner pyramidal cell layer – The superficial part contains medium sized pyramidal cells and the deep part accommodates large pyramidal cells and inner layer of Baillarger (horizontally directed fibers). Large pyramidal cells are called **cells of Betz**.

6. Fusiform cell layer – It comprises of fusiform and stellate cells of different shapes and sizes along with plenty of fibers as well as cells of Martinotti, axons of which project vertically upward to ramify in the molecular layer.

Hippocampus and dentate gyrus

This is phylogenetically older part of the brain and comprises of only three layers. These are molicular layer, pyramidal cell layer and pleomorphic layer.

3
CARDIOVASCULAR AND LYMPHATIC SYSTEM

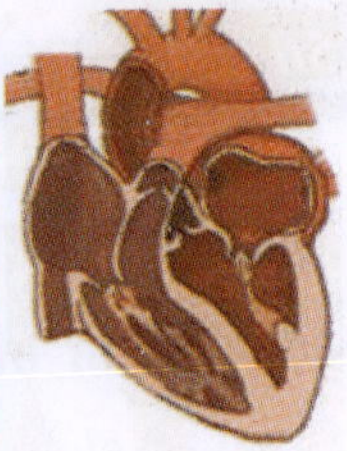

This system comprises of the following components :

Heart	Lymph vessels
Artery	Lymph node
Vein	Spleen
Capillary	Thymus ; Tonsils

HEART

The wall of the heart is composed of three layers of tissues.

a) Epicardium,

b) Myocardium,

c) Endocardium.

Epicardium

It is a serous membrane and the visceral layer of pericardium, that immediately envelops the heart. It is composed of a superficial layer of mesothelium over a thin layer of connective tissue. This layer contains blood capillaries, lymphatic capillaries and some nerves. Its deeper layer contains blood vessels and fat and is continuous with endomysium of the underlying cardiac muscle.

Myocardium

This is the thickest layer and composed spirally arranged cardiac muscle. (already described).

Endocardium

It is the innermost tunic of heart and is composed of endothelium, a single layer of squamous cells and sub-endothelial connective tissue. It not only lines the atrial and ventricular chambers, but covers all the structures that extend from the heart walls such as chordae tendinae, valves, papillary muscle, etc. The deep (outer) layer may contain some smooth muscle fibers in some places. Generally its thickness has a inverse relation with the thickness of myocardium.

Valves of heart are formed by the foldings of endocardium with a core of dense fibroclastic tissue.

Skeleton of heart

The skeleton of heart comprises of a) four fibrous rings at the wall of four orifices (2 atrio-ventricular orifices, aortic orifice and pulmonary orifice); b) membranous part of interventricular septum and c) two fibrous trigones those connect the fibrous rings.

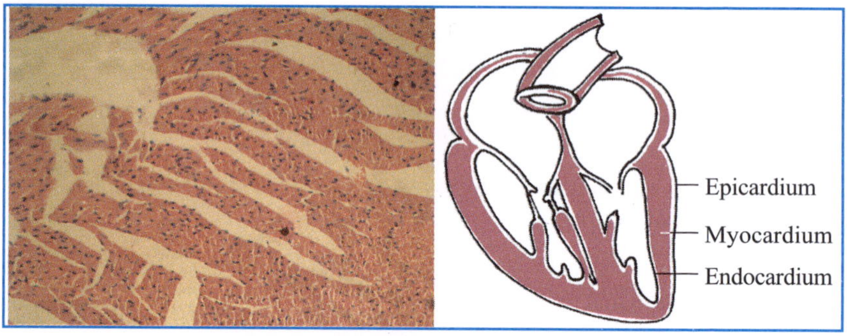

Fig. 3.1 Low power photomicrograph showing disposition of cardiac muscle.

ARTERY

These are the musculo-membranous tubes, receive the blood from the heart and carry it to the capillaries. Arteries have been classified into three groups : a) Elastic artery, b) Muscular artery and c) Arteriole.

However the wall of all these vessels have the following common structure of variable proportions.

i) ***Tunica adventitia*** – This is the outermost thin coat of the wall and composed of fine elastic and collagen fibers. The collagen fibers are

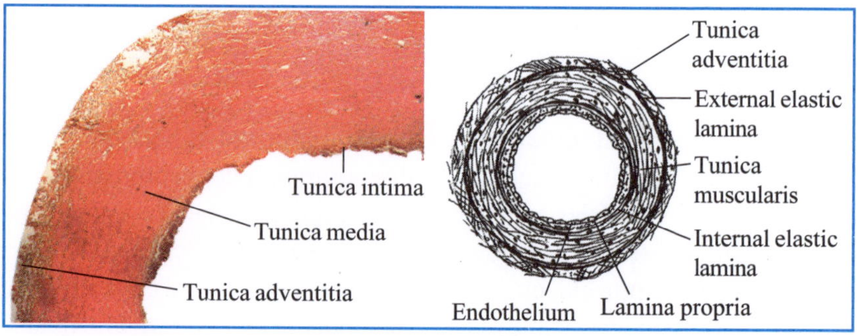

Fig. 3.2 Cross section of a medium-sized artery.

generally arranged parallel to the long axis of the vessels. This layer attaches the vessels with the surrounding connective tissue and retains the tunica media and intima during distension.

ii) ***Tunica media*** – This forms the bulk of the wall and composed of circularly arranged smooth muscle fibers and some elastic fibers. The concentration of elastic fibers is much towards the periphery and forms an external elastic lamina which separates this layer from the tunica adventitia.

iii) ***Tunica intima*** – This is the innermost coat of the wall and composed of a) single layer of squamous cells (endothelium), b) Lamina propria, composed of longitudinally arranged delicate collagen and elastic fibers and c) Internal elastic lamina, formed by the condensation of elastic fibers. This layer of tunica intima maintains the potency of the lumen of the arteries.

Structural variations amongst the three type of arteries.

	Elastic artery	***Muscular artery***	***Arteriole***
	Large arteries, close to heart (Conducting artery).	Large and medium artery (Distributing artery).	Small muscular arteries about 100μ in diameter (Resistance arteries).
Tunica Adventitia	Thin	Thicker	Very thin
Tunica Media	Thick elastic fibers are more in amount.	Very thick smooth muscle fibers are more in amount.	Thick elastic fibers disappear and smooth muscles are prominent.
Tunica Intima	Smooth. Small folds are absent. Lamina propria is thick. Internal elastic lamina is very thin.	Exhibits small folds. Lamina propria is thin. Internal elastic lamina is prominent.	Exhibits small folds. Internal elastic lamina is thin.

Capallaries

These are the finest blood vessels, form diffuse network by branching and anastomosing within themselves and link between arterioles and venules. The capillaries have the following characteristics :

a) These are microscopic vessels with an average diameter of about 8 to 10 microns.

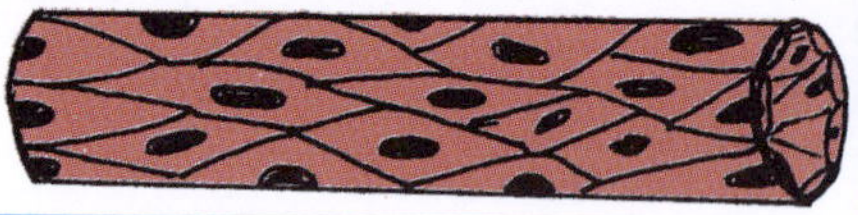

Fig. 3.3 Capillary.

b) The wall is composed of a single layer of endothelial cells with elongated nucleus and surrounded by a thin basal lamina. Some flat mesenchymal cells with long cytoplasmic processes remain associated with the basal lamina, known as ***pericytes***.

c) In muscle and nerve tissue, the wall of the capillaries are uniform and without any pore. These are called ***Muscular capillaries***.

The capillaries of the glomerulus of kidneys and those of endocrine glands possess small pores. They are known as ***Fenestrated Capillaries***.

VEINS

These are the thin walled blood vessels and more numerous. They start from periphery, gradually increase in caliber along their course towards heart. Although the wall is thin, the lumen is large in comparison to the arteries.

The wall of the veins have the following characteristics :

i) ***Tunica adventitia*** – It is composed of longitudinally arranged collagen fibers, some elastic fibers and some smooth muscle fibers. This layer is thickest of the three coats.

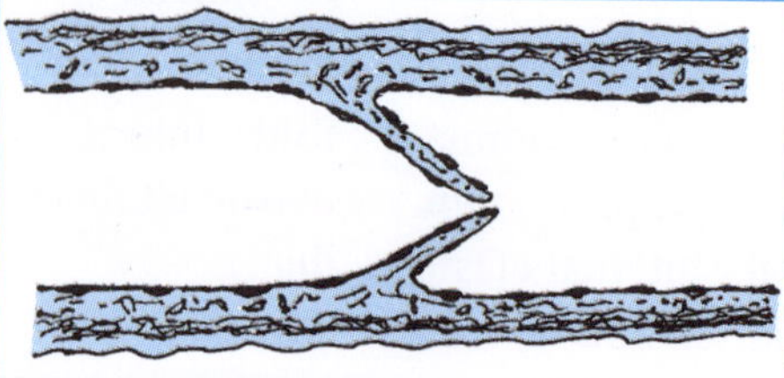

Fig. 3.4 Vein.

ii) ***Tunica media*** – This is thin and is composed of collagen fibers, elastic fibers and some smooth muscle fibers,

iii) ***Tunica intima*** – The structure of this layer is almost similar to that of arteries but the elastic lamina is absent. The veins of limbs have valves in their lumen which are inclined towards the direction of the flow of blood and prevent back flow. These valves are formed by the foldings of tunica intima.

Smooth muscle fibers are absent in the veins of CNS and bone marrow. However some veins like uterine veins during pregnancy, pulmonary veins and veins of penis contain little amount of smooth muscle fibers in tunica media.

Sinusoids

These are dilated vascular channels lined by an incomplete layer of endothelium and basal lamina and therefore allow the blood to come in direct contact with the cells of the tissue. These are found in *liver*, *spleen*, *bone marrow* and in *some endocrine glands*.

The lining membrame contains some phagocytic R. E cells or fixed macrophages. Since the wall of the sinusoids have gaps in some places and flow of blood through these spaces is slow, considerable exchange of metabolites between the blood and surrounding tissue takes place in the sinusoids.

The sinusoids may connect an arteriole with a venule, e.g. spleen and a venule to another venule, e.g. liver.

Vasa Vesorum

These are the vessels for large blood vessels. They supply and drain the outer part of tunica media and tunica adventitia of large and medium blood vessels.

Arterio – Venous anastomosis

Bypassing the capillary network, some direct communication between arterioles and venules, are found in some places of the body. The wall of this communicating zone of the vessels is thick and richly supplied with sympathetic nerves. They are found in skin, erectile tissue of external genitalia and in G.I. tract. Some such anastomotic vessels are tortuous and thick walled and contain modified muscle (epitheloid) cells called Glomus.

Lymph Vessels

The excess tissue fluid which do not return via capillaries and venules, are carried through separate channels are known as lymph vessels.

Lymph is a colourless fluid which contains small amount of plasma protein and lymphocytes. These lymphocytes are added to the fluid while it circulates through lymph nodes.

The lymphatic vessels are small, delicate thin tubes possess numerous valves which allow the lymph to flow in one direction. These are mainly distributed in the mucous, serous and synovial membromes, glands and in the skin but ***not found in the nervous tissue***. The flow of the lymph is very slow. The vessels pass through lymph nodes and finally end at the thoralic duct and right lymphatic duct which open into the venous system.

Lymph capillaries

These are blind ended small vessels originate from the tissue spaces and are lined by a single layer of endothelial cells.

Larger lymph Vessels

Lymph capillaries join to form larger vessels. The wall of these vessels is composed of three coats like that of venules, These vessels come and enter lymph nodes on their way as afferents.

Lymphocytes

These are one type of agranular white blood cells having a dark spherical large nucleus that occupies almost the entire cell. Some lymphocytes are large and some are small in size. They can identify foreign antigens and help in the production of antibodies. Functionally two types – T-lymphocytes and B-lymphocytes are present in the body. In routine histology these two types of cells cannot be identified separately but can be identified with the help of immuno-histochemistry.

T- lymphocytes (Thymus dependent) after their origin in the bone marrow, go to the thymus. Here they differentiate further, become mature and transported to the circulation and other lymphoid organs. Lymphatics leave the node as efferent vessels.

B-Lymphocytes (Bursa dependent) – The name of these cells is derived from the Bursa of Fabricious of birds, where they differentiate. But in mammals, there is no bursa of fabricious and these cells differentiate only from bone marrow.

Lactials – The villi of small intestine contain a lymph capillary in their cores, known as lactials. These are useful at the time of abosorption of fatty acids from the intestine.

Thoracic duct – The structure of this largest lymph vessel resembles that of a vein but contain more muscle fibers in the tunica media.

Lymphoid tissue

This is the aggregation of lymphocytes within a network of reticular tissue. The lymphocytes may be matured or in the different stages of maturation.

When this aggregation is found to be spread over an area below the epithelium of G.I. tract or Respiratory tract in little irregular manner, called Diffuse lymphoid tissue.

In some places these lymphoid tissues remain in the form of a small rounded masses. They are called **lymph follicles** or **lymph nodules**. Peyer's patches of the small intestine are good examples.

Some of these lymph nodule contains a central zone of loosely packed lymphoblasts and a peripheral zone of densely packed small lymphocytes. The central loose area is called germinal center. These lymphoid tissues are very much prominent in the ileum.

LYMPH NODES

They are oval or bean shaped nodular brown or reddish black structures of variable sizes ranging from very minute bodies to the size of a lemon. The hilum is in a depressed area where blood vessels and efferent lymph vessels enter or leave the gland. The afferent vessels are found at different points along the convex surface of the node. The nodes are covered by a connective tissue ***capsule***. The capsule send septa or trabeculae inside the node. The trabeculae form compartments at the cortical area. The compartments accommodate cortical nodules or follicles. The central portion of a

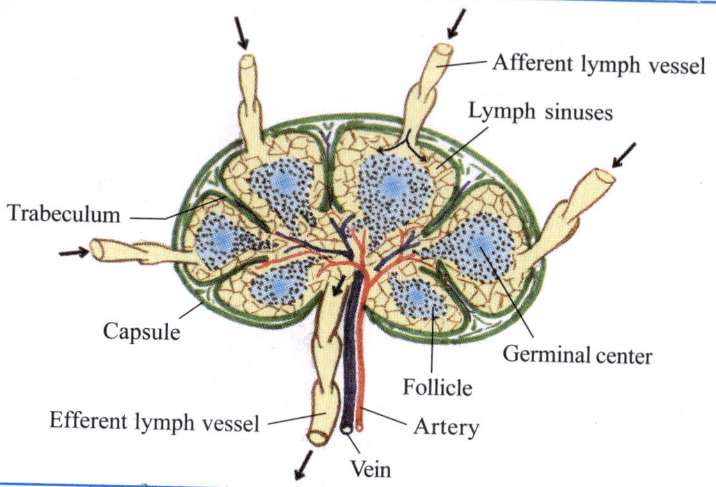

Fig. 3.5 Section of a Lymph node (diagramatic).

follicle is known as **germinal center**. The germinal center is lighter in colour and the place for production of lymphocytes. The cortical nodules are separated from the capsule as well as trabeculae by lymph sinuses. The medulla is composed of lymph cords which extend from the nodules, lymphocytes, RE cells, meshwork of trabeculae and lymph sinuses. The lymph enter the nodes through afferent lymphatics, percolate through sinusoids and the filtered lymph emerges via the efferent lymphatic through the hilus.

Although variable in number, the lymph nodes are constantly found in certain definite areas of the body, such as axilla, inguinal region, mesentery, etc.

SPLEEN

This is the largest lymphoid organ. It produces erythrocytes in fetal life and lymphocytes after birth and therefore it is also called an haemo-lymph organ. It filters blood and remove foreign particles from circulating blood.

Framework of the organ

(a) **Capsule** – The spleen is covered by a thick capsule which is composed of collagen and elastic fibers and some smooth muscle fibers. The capsule remains covered by visceral peritoneum.

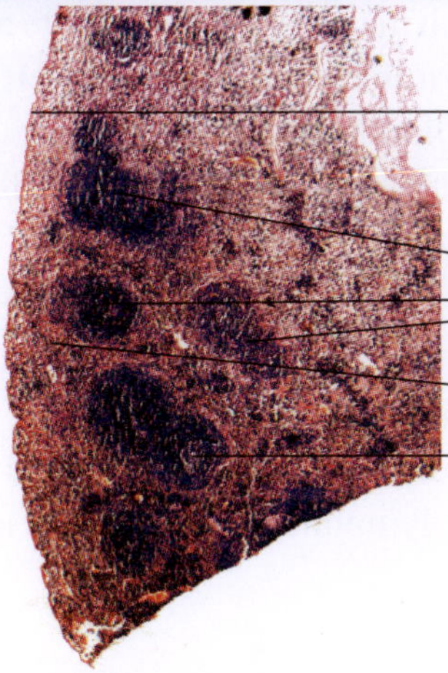

Fig. 3.6 Section of spleen.

1. White pulps are in the form of round/oval masses (deep stained);
2. Red pulp is the background red zone ;
3. Germinal centers are clear.

(b) **Trabeculae** – These are the septa which extend from the capsule and hylum towards the interior. These trabeculae branch and join each other and divide the gland into a number of lobules. Composition of these septa is similar to that of the capsule.

(c) **Connective tissue network** – The spaces between the trabeculae has a net work of reticular connective tissue to hold the lymphoid tissue in position. There is no cortex and medulla in this organ.

In freshly cut large tissue pieces of spleen exhibit pale and red zones at the surface on naked eye observation. The pale zones which remain scattered in a red background is called white pulp and the background red zone is called red pulp.

Lymphoid tissue of spleen

The substance of the spleen comprises of lymphoid tissue and blood vessels within reticular framework.

White pulp

In histological sections (H&E) it is found that numerous deep stained round or oval masses of lymphoid tissue are scattered unevenly within the background of lighter zone. Each such mass contains a minute artery at the center. Some of them have germinal centers. These circular masses are known as white pulps. The blood vessel may sometimes be eccentric in position. In the germinal center B-lymphocytes proliferate.

T-lymphocytes are found in the periphery.

Red Pulp

The rest of the zone comprises of venous sinusoids, spongy net work of connective tissue elements, lymphoid tissue, circulating blood cells and some macrophages. Both B and T lymphocytes are found in red pulp.

Spleenic circulation

Branches of spleenic artery leave the trabeculae and subdivide to form arterioles. Each arteriole passes through the white pulp and again divides into smaller but straight vessels within the red-pulp area. These are known as **Penicillar arteries**. The tunica adventitia is lost in the white –pulp. The penicillar arteries loose their tunica media in the red-pulp and become ensheathed by reticular cells and form spindle shaped thickening called **Ellipsoids**. The lumen at the ellipsoid zone become narrow. The extensions of the penicillar arteries after ellipsoids, become narrow and form the arterial capillaries. These capillaries may be directly continuous with the venous sinusoids as per close theory of circulation.

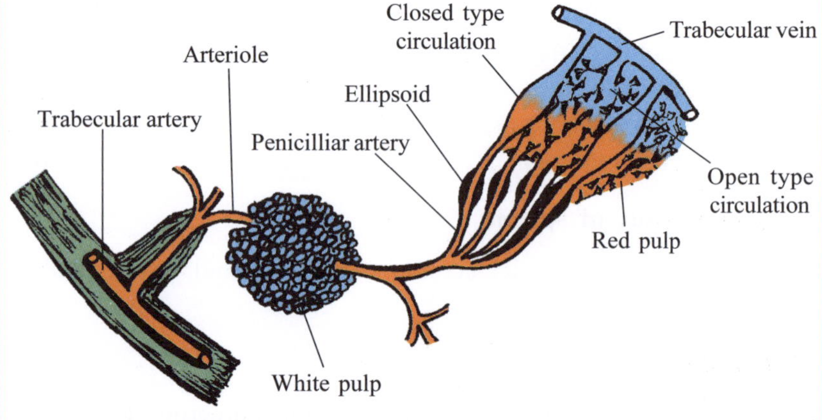

Fig. 3.7 Spleenic circulation.

As per open theory of circulation the capillaries open directly into the splenic cords of red pulp and from there the blood cells percolate into the venous sinusoids. However, there is a general agreement that the sinusoidal endothelium has large gaps in them and when the organ remain in relaxed condition, allow the blood to go in and out of the sinusoids to the surrounding red pulp. During contraction, these gaps are closed and blood flows from capillaries to veules directly.

Haemal nodes

These are small dark coloured haemolymph nodules contain an admixture of blood and lymph which fillup the interstices of reticular fibers. However these nodes are rare in man.

THYMUS

This is an irregular bi-lobed structure situated in the cranial mediastinum in front of the aortic arch. It is a lympho-epithelial organ. Its epithelial part is derived from the 3rd pharyngeal pouch and the lymphoid part is derived from mesoderm. This is an important organ for body defense mechanism. In early life it is developed. It progressly increases up to the age of puberty and thereafter regesses and

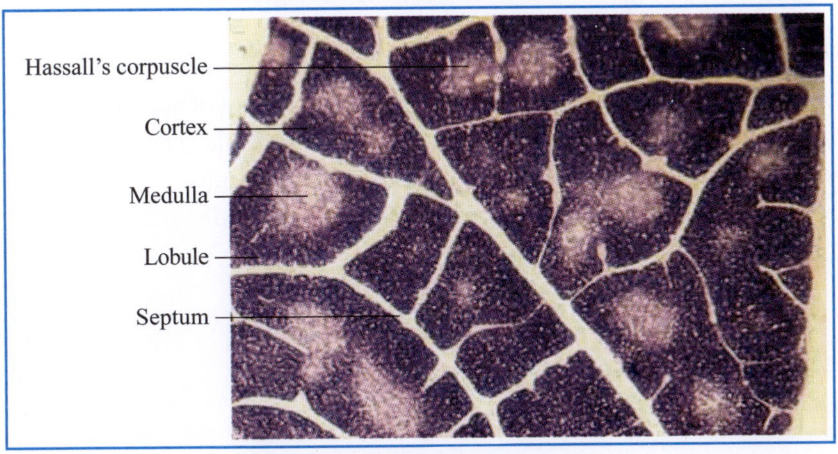

Fig. 3.8 Section of thymus.

1. Cortical lobules are incomplete ;
2. Hassal's corpuscles are present in few of the lobules ;
3. Agrigation of lymphocytes are found in the cortex of the lobules.

undergoes involution and converted to a fibro-fatty mass in elder subject.

Capsule – The structure is encapsulated by a thin layer of connective tissue which is composed of collagen and elastic fibers. Thin septa extend form the capsule and divide the cortex into numerous incomplete lobules.

Parenchyma – In the cortex lobules are situated. Each lobule has a peripheral more condenced zone called the cortex and a loose central zone with scanty thymocytes and more epithelial cells, called medulla. The cortex is primarily composed of aggregated lymphocytes (T-cells) and few macro-phages.

Medulla contains lightly packed lymphocytes, blood vessels and epitheloid mesh. Actually the original medulla of the organ branch towards the periphery and invaginate into the incomplete cortical lobules to form the medulla of the lobules. Therefore the medulla of the lobules are the extensions of the original medulla of the organ like the white matter of cerebellum. Degenerated epithelial cells form nest-like structures, consist of several layers of concentrically arranged flattend cells around a central hyaline necrotic mass called **Hassall's corpuscle**. These corpuscles increase in number with the advancement of age.

Tonsils

These are the lumps of lymphoid tissues in the form of nodules situated under the epithelium and are partly covered by capsule. They are mostly situated in the proximal parts of digestive and respiratory system. They remain separated from the surrounding tissue by a distinct connective tissue layer.

4

INTEGUMENTARY SYSTEM

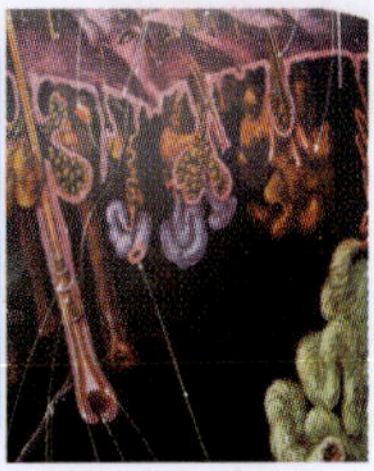

Integument is a multilayered covering of the body and composed of skin and subcutaneous tissue. Integument is responsible for i) Providing protection from mechanical objects as well as from entry of micro organisms and from ultraviolet rays, ii) Regulating of body temperature, iii) Excreting of some waste products, iv) Providing sites for synthesis of vitamin D and v) Playing active role in sensory perception. The complexion of integument depends on the absence and presence of Melanin. Presence of breakdown products of hemoglobin in the circulation may also influence skin colour.

SKIN

The skin comprises Epidermis and Dermis.

Epidermis

The Epidermis is the outer epithelial portion of skin and composed of the following layers of cells.

(a) Stratum basale
(b) Stratum spinosum
(c) Stratum Granulosum
(d) Stratum lucidum
(e) Stratum corneum

The ***Stratum Basale*** is the innermost layer of epidermis and composed of a layer of moderately large columnar cells. The basal cell are anchored in the basement membrane by fringe like processes and adhere with each other by desmosomes. In some places dendritic ***Melanocytes*** are present in between the basal cells. These cells provide pigment granules to the basal cells. During proliferation the melanocytes carry pigment to the higher cells. Frequently this layer invaginates into the depressions of dermis. These finger like invaginations are called epidermal papillae and therefore this layer of cells gives a wavy appearance in histological sections.

The ***Stratum Spinosum*** is a thick zone and composed of multiple layers of polyhedral cells. The cells have spine like processes in their surfaces and therefore called ***Pricle cells***.

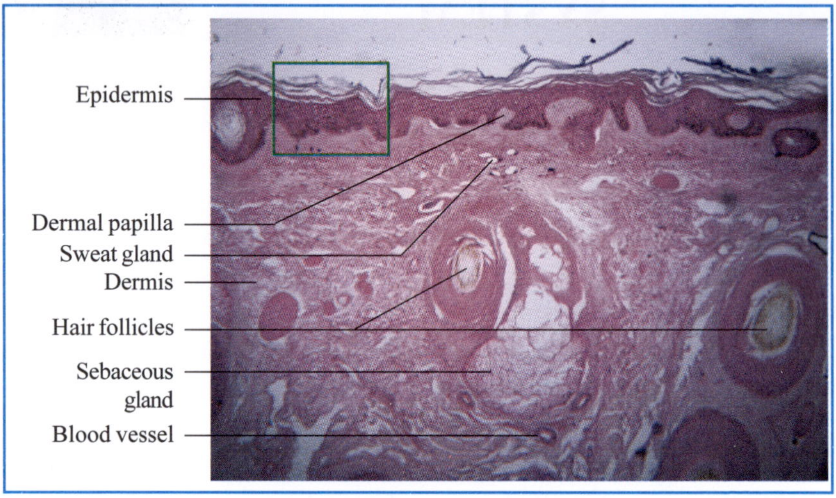

Fig. 4.1a Section of skin.

1. Epidermis with its all layers are visible ;
2. Hair follicles and associated sebaceous glands are prominent ;
3. Sweat gland is found in the form of several hollow spaces ;
4. Dermal papillae and vessels are clear.

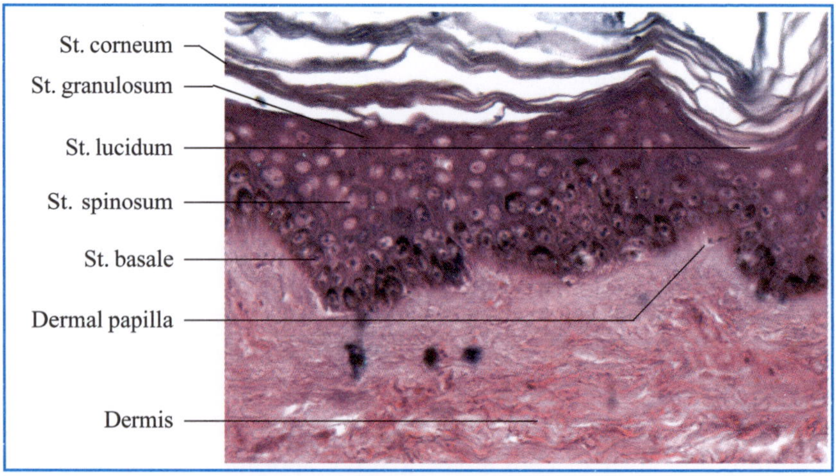

Fig. 4.1b Inset figure (Epidermis, higher magnification).

These spines are actually tonofibrils which randomly occur in the cytoplasm, radiate from the surface and make intercellular bridges in between the cells.

Mitosis occurs in both the cells of stratum basale and stratum spinosum and therefore these two layers together are called ***stratum germinativum***.

Stratum Granulosum is composed of one to few layers of flattened granule containing cells. Actually, as a result of growth process at the stratum germinativum, the cells of the peripheral zone are pushed towards the surface. These cells become flattened, move further away from the dermal capillaries, get less nutrition and therefore synthesise highly basophilic keratohyaline granules by recycling nucleic acids.

Stratum Lucidum – This is an inconstant layer and found only in the thick epidermis. It is composed of dying or closely packed dead cells of the periphery of the granulosum cells and therefore the nuclei are not apparent. This layer appear as a thin homogenous refractive (Lucid) zone in between the stratum granulosum and stratum corneum and thus named Lucidum.

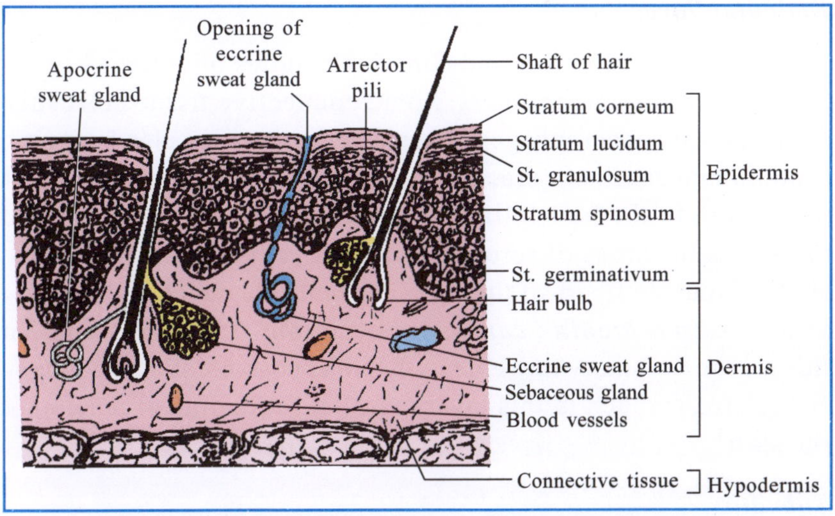

Fig. 4.2 Microscopic structure of Skin (Diagramatic).

Stratum corneum – Several layers of flattend cornified plates of dead cells form this most superficial layer of epidermis. Here the cells are transformed into a horny material called keratin.

Keratin is an albuminoid protein in the form of fibers derived from stratified squamous epethelia. This is hard, elastic and resistant to friction. In some places like nails, the keratin is hardest. The hardness is due to more sulfur content of the tissue.

Dermis (corium)

The connective tissue layer below epidermis is the dermis. It contains blood vessels, lymphatics, nerve fibers, hair follicles, sebaceous glands, sweat gland, bundles of collagen fibers and network of reticular fibers. There are two layers of the dermis – outer papillary layer and inner reticular layer.

Papillary layer

It is the superficial layer and forms finger like projections of different shape and sizes which interdigitate with the downward projections of epidermal papillae. The dermal papillae contain blood vessels and nerve endings (touch receptors).

Reticular layer

This is the deep layer and contains bundles of collagen fibers and network of elastic fibers. Some connective tissue cells such as fibroblasts, macrophages, plasma cells, etc. may also be found. Smooth muscle fibers(erector pilorum or erector pili) are present in relation to the hair follicles. These muscle fibers are present mainly in the areas of scrotum, teat and penis. In some animals, skeletal muscle fibers of the cutaneous muscle which is popularly known as ***panniculus carnosus***, penetrate the dermis and for this reason voluntary movement of skin is possible. Some collagen fibers are arranged in this layer, parallel to the line of tension of the skin.

Subcutis

This is a layer of connective tissue attaches the dermis with the underlying muscles or sclerous tissue. It is composed of loose collagen and elastic fibers. Adipose tissue in the form of clusters may be present.

APPENDAGES OF SKIN

These are the specialized structures generally derived from the epidermis and serve specific functions. These are i) Sweat glands, ii) Sebaceous glands, iii) hair, iv) nail, v) Arrector pilli muscles.

i) *Sweat gland*

These are simple coiled tubular glands and Merocrine in nature and also called **eccrine glands**. The secretary portion of the coiled gland is situated deep into the reticular layer of the dermis. The coiled tube is lined by a single layer of high cuboidal secretory cells. Some spirally arranged cells remain in between the epithelial cells and basement membrane are the myoepithelial cells. The duct of the gland experience a helical course through the epidermis and is lined by a double layer of cuboidal cells and open onto the skin surface. These glands are distributed in entire body surface.

Apocrine type of sweat glands are present on mons pubis, axilla, areola of the breast, etc. The secretion of these glands start after puberty and responsible for the characteristic body odour. Ducts of apocrine glands open in the apical part of hair follicles. Ceruminous glands are also apocrine sweat glands.

ii) *Sebaceous gland*

These are simple or branched alveolar glands and Holocrine in nature. The alveoli open into a common duct and release the secretion, sebum, into the hair follicle. They are mostly associated with the hair follicles and invade the dermis. However in hairless zone the duct of the gland open directly into the skin.

Each alveolus is surrounded by a basal lamina upon which a layer of cuboidal cells are present. These cells enlarge, become polygonal in shape, pushed towards the center and finally disintegrate to form sebum. The duct of this gland is short and lined by stratified squamous epithelium.

The population of these glands is highly variable in different zones of the body and are absent in soles, palms and flexure surface of the digits. These glands are mostly found on the face, scalp, ear, nostrils, around the anus and vulva. They are not much active before puberty.

iii) *Hair*

Hairs are flexible filamentous thread like keratinized structures and distributed all over the body. However, they are absent on the lips, nipples, palms, soles, glans penis, prepuce and labia minora. They grow from the hair follicles, situated in the dermis. The hairs are sensory in nature and act as heat insulators.

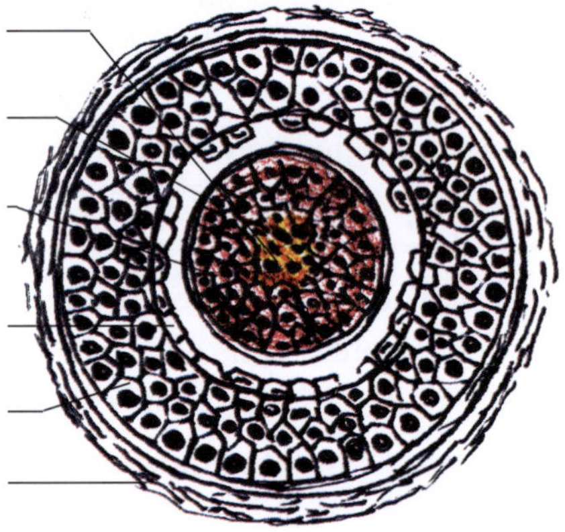

Fig. 4.3 Hair follicle (Transverse section).

Structure of hair – It has mainly two parts : a) shaft and b) root.

(a) ***Staft*** is the free part of the hair which remains above the surface of the skin. It is composed of an outermost keratinized layer called **cuticle**, a layer of densely packed keratinized cells called cortex and a central zone of loose cells known as medulla. The cells of the medulla are mostly cuboidal in shape and have spaces in between them. Both the cell group contain keratin and melanosome.

(b) ***Root*** – The part of the hair which remains embedded within the skin in a tubular sheath is known as root.

The deep end of the embedded root expands like a cup, known as hair bulb. The bulb is invaded by a papilla of connective tissue, called hair papilla. The down growth of the epidermis which encloses the root of the hair is known as **external root sheath**. At the deeper part another layer appear close to the root is called **Internal root sheath**. The hair bulb, hair papilla, the internal root sheath and the external root sheath together from the Hair follicle.

The external hair sheath is derived from stratum corneum and stratum spinosum of epidermis. During the formation of a hair follicle, growth of the cells of epidermis occurs into the dermis as well as into the subcutaneous tissue. The internal root sheath is composed of an inner cuticular layer, middle granular epithelial layer and an outer pale epithelial layer.

The cluster of epithelial cells at the deepest part of the down growth of epidermis which gets tissue fluid from the hair papilla and is responsible for the formation and growth of the hair is known as **germinal matrix**.

iv) *Nail*

Nail is developed from stratum lucidum of epidermis. It consists of several layers of flat transparent cornified cells which has been transformed to keratin. The nail bed which supports the nail consists of stratum granulosum of epidermis and the dermis. The body of the nail is free part and the root is the proximal part which remains covered by skin. Nail matrix is the part of the nail bed near the root. The parts of a nail are root, body and tip. The root is the proximal part and remains embedded under the *proximal nail fold* and its extension over the body called *Eponychium*. It rests on the germinal matrix which forms nail plate by the proliferation of epidermal cells. The body rests on *nail bed* which is formed by stratum germinativum and corium. The distal border of the nail is connected to the underlying epidermis by a fold called *Hyponychium*.

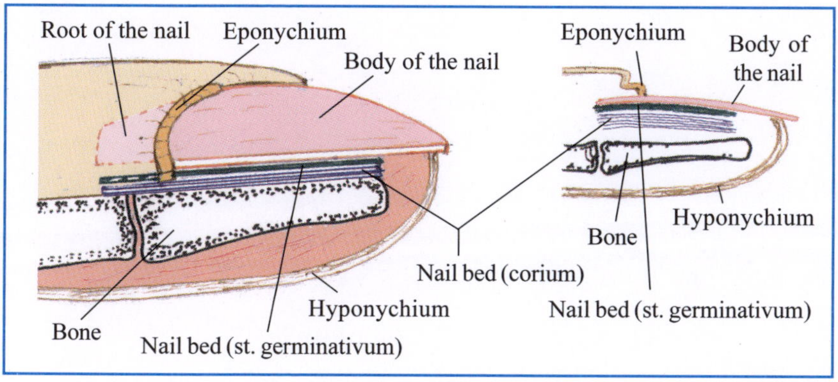

Fig. 4.4 Structure of a nail.

v) *Arrector pilorum muscles*

These are very small bundle of muscle fibers which extend from the papillary layer of dermis to the fibrous sheath of hair follicle. These muscles are innervated with the sympathetic nerves. Contraction of these muscles leads to the rise of hairs.

Nerves and vessels of skin

Since the skin is an important sensory organ, it is richly supplied with nerves. Sensory nerve fibers from free nerve endings are innervating the dermis as well as epidermis. Efferent sympathetic fibers supply the arrector pilli muscles, sweat glands and smooth muscles of blood vessels.

Numerous fine blood vessels are distributed within the dermis. Epidermis is avascular and therefore the cells of this layer derive their nutrition from the vessels of dermis.

5

DIGESTIVE SYSTEM

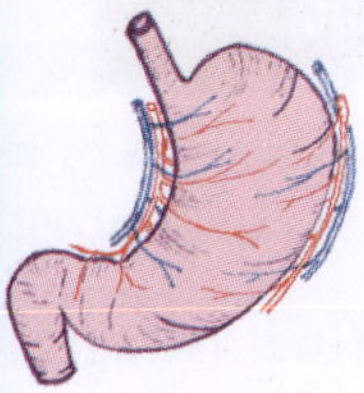

This system is associated with the ingestion, digestion and absorption of food and elimination of waste products. Basically this system is formed by a muscular tube which starts at the month, undergoes regional modification and specialization according to the functional need and terminates at the anus.

The components of this system are as follows :

Mouth	Salivary glands
Pharynx	Pancreas
Esophagus	Liver
Stomach	
Small Intestine	
Large Intestine	

MOUTH (ORAL CAVITY)

Lips – The main bulk of the lip is contributed by the tunica muscularis, which is composed of the striated muscle fibers of Orbicularis oris.

Externally the lips are covered by skin and internally lined by mucous membrane. At the junction of the skin and nucous membrane, the hair follicles are absent but the epidermis is thick. The mucous membrane is generally made up of non-keratinised stratified squamous epithelium which tends to be keratinised in areas subject to considerable friction. Demarcation between lamina propria and submucosa is indistinct. Labial glands are serous or seromucous type.

Cheeks – Histological structure of the cheeks are more or less similar to that of lips. They are also composed of skin, muscles, glands and mucous membrane. Skin is continuous with the other part of the face. Muscular layer. is formed by buccinator, levator and depressor muscles of the face. Buccal glands are minor salivary glands situated at the submucosa as well as within the muscle bundles. These glands are serous or mucous or mixed type. The lining mucous membrane is made up of non keratinized squamous epithelium.

Gum (Gingiva)

It is composed of a thick layers of collagen and elastic fibers which are closely attached to the periosteum of the alveoli bearing bones and surrounds the neck of the tooth. Many fibers of gingival lamina propria are continuous with the periodontal membrane and are inserted into the cementum. The epithelium is frequently Keratinised. The lamina propria contains many lymphocytes.

Hard Palate

The muscous membrane is composed of non-keratinized stratified squamous epithelium but tends to be keratinized in areas subject to considerable friction. Lamina propria is well developed and papillary processes from this layer extend into the thickness of the stratified squamous epithelium. The submucosa is composed of dense network of collagen and reticular fibers. This layer blends with the periosteum.

Soft Palate

The mucous membrane is made up of stratified squamous noncornified epithelium. The mucous membrane of the nasal surface is composed of ciliated pseudostratified columnar epithelium. Branched tubulo acinar mucous and seromucous glands are present in the lamina propria and submucosa. The bulk of the soft palate which remain between two mucous membranes, is composed of longitudinally oriented striated muscle fibers and connective tissue.

TONGUE

This highly movable muscular structure. This structure is covered at its dorsal aspect by a specialized mucous membrane and contains plenty of vessels, nerves, connective tissue, glands and some spindle shaped Neuro-epithelial (taste) cells. These taste cells have microvilli at their tips which project through a small opening on the surface of the tongue, called taste pore. The base of these cells are associated with the sensory nerve terminals.

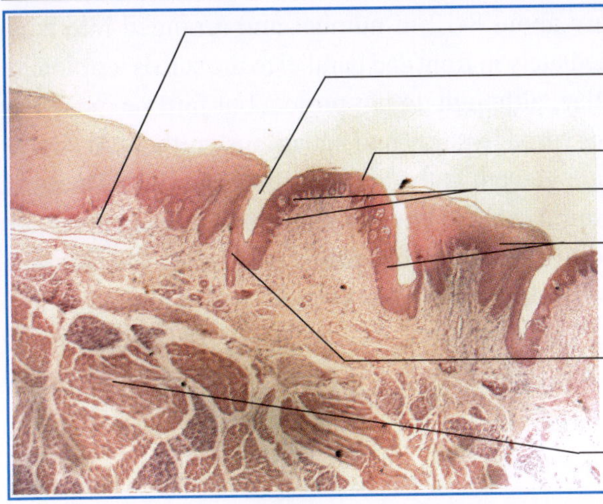

Fig. 5.1 Section of a tongue.

1. The surface is covered by stratified squamous epithelium ;
2. Taste buds are seen within the covering epithelium of vallate papilla ;
3. The fibers of the musculature is arranged in different directions.

The tunica mucosa of the dorsal surface is formed by stratified squamous epithelium. Thin surface contains many macroscopic papillae which either serves mechanical or gustatory function. These are – a) filliform, b) fungiform, c) vallate and d) follicle.

Filliform papillae – These are numerous fine variety blunt cone shaped papillae and are distributed throughout the dorsal surface of the anterior two third of the tongue. They are devoid of taste buds. The tips of these papillae project above the surface and are covered by keratinized stratified squamous epithelium. The stratum corneum is thick. Each papilla has a connective tissue core which is highly vascular.

Fungiform papillae – They are less in number but larger in size and remain scattered among the filliform papillae along the sides and tip of the tongue. The shape of these papillae look like young mushroom and hence called fungiform papillae. Non keratinized stratified squamous epithelium covers the surfaces of these papillae. The epithelium contains few taste buds.

Vallate papillae – They are the largest variety of papillae of tongue and each of them is encircled by a wall and therefore also called circumvallate. They are about 8-12 in number and arranged into a V-shaped single row immediately in front and parallel to the sulcus terminalis. The tips of these papillae, although do not project but fairly exposed to the surface. They are covered by stratified squamous epithelium. Good number of taste buds are present at the sides of these papillae. Ducts of some small gustatory serous glands Von-Ebner's gland open in the inner surface of the surrounding wall. The connective tissue core is dense and rich in blood vessels and nerves.

Foliate papillae – These are three or more parallel folds of the mucosa situated on either side of root and in front of anterior pillars. Stratified squamous epithelium covers these papillae. Some taste buds are found in the epithelium.

Taste buds

These are oval elongated structures situated within the covering epithelium of fungiform, vallate and foliate papillae of tongue and extend

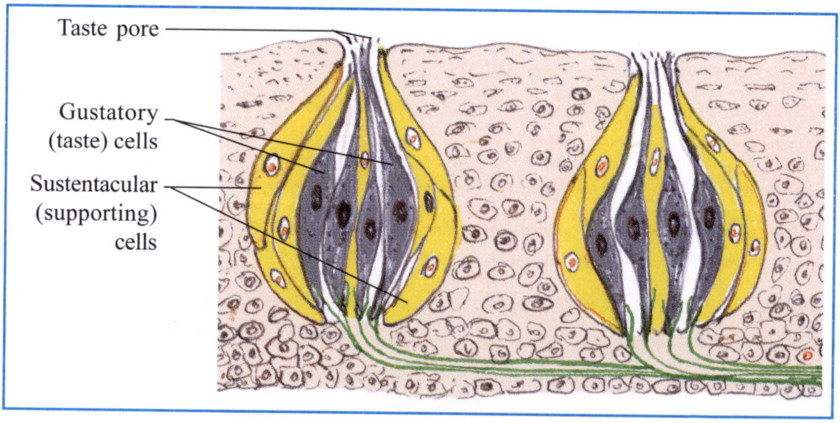

Fig. 5.2 Taste buds (diagramatic).

from the basement membrane to the surface. The buds are flask shaped structures with a base, wide body and neck which opens at the **taste pore**. Each bud is composed of spindle shaped taste cells or the gustatory cells at the center and crescent shaped supporting cells. The taste cells are neuro-epithelial receptor cells and are connected to sensory fibers. It is evident that the life span of those taste cells is short and the degenerated cells are regularly replaced by peripheral germinal cells.

The taste buds are also found in the soft palate, epiglottis and in other areas of mouth.

Musculature

The bulk of the tongue is formed by the intrinsic muscles mainly and extrinsic muscles partly. All are striated muscle fibers. The intringic muscles fiber bundles are arranged longitudinally, transversely and vertically. The dorsal logitudinal fibers are situated below the mucosa. Due to excessive mobility of the organ, the muscle fibers are arranged in multiple directions.

Ventral surface of the tongue – This surface is smooth and is covered by non keratinized stratified squamous epithelium. This epithelium is highly vascular.

Glands

Some seromucous lingual glands are present between the bundles of muscle fibers in a scattered manner. These are small lobulated glands and part of minor salivary glands of the tongue.

Lingual tonsil : The mucosa of the posterior one third of the tongue is devoid of papillae and is separated from the underlying muscle by a loose submucous coat. This submucous coat contains mucous and serous glands and numerous lymphatic follicles known as **lingual tonsil**.

TOOTH

Most of the mammals are ***diphyodonty*** and possess two dentitions. The first set which appear at the beginning is called deciduous or milk teeth and the second or permanent teeth appear later and replace milk teeth. However both types of teeth bear similar micro-anatomical structure. Rat amongst mammals is incidentally monophyodont. Teeth are highly mineralized and hardest structure of the body and implanted into the alveolar sockets of the upper and lower jaw bones. The exposed portion of a tooth which is covered by very hard translucent material (enamel) is known as body or ***crown***. The implanted narrow part which is covered by a narrow yellowish material (cementum) known as ***root***. The junction between the crown and root is called

neck. A tooth is composed of a pulp cavity, dentin enamel and cementum.

Pulp cavity

It is a small cavity inside the body of the tooth. It is little dilated towards the crown and narrow towards the root. The narrow portion open at the tip of this root in the from of a canal known as root canal. The cavity is lined by a layer of tall cells called ***odontoblasts***. The pulp is composed of connective tissue cells, blood vessels, nerve and collagen fibers. The vessels and nerves pass into the pulp cavity through the root canal.

Dentin

The bulk of the tooth is formed by dentin which also encloses the pulp cavity. Dentin contains numerous parallely arranged dentinal canaliculi in which dentinal fibers or processes extend from the tall odontoblast cells of the pulp cavity towards the periphery in a radiating

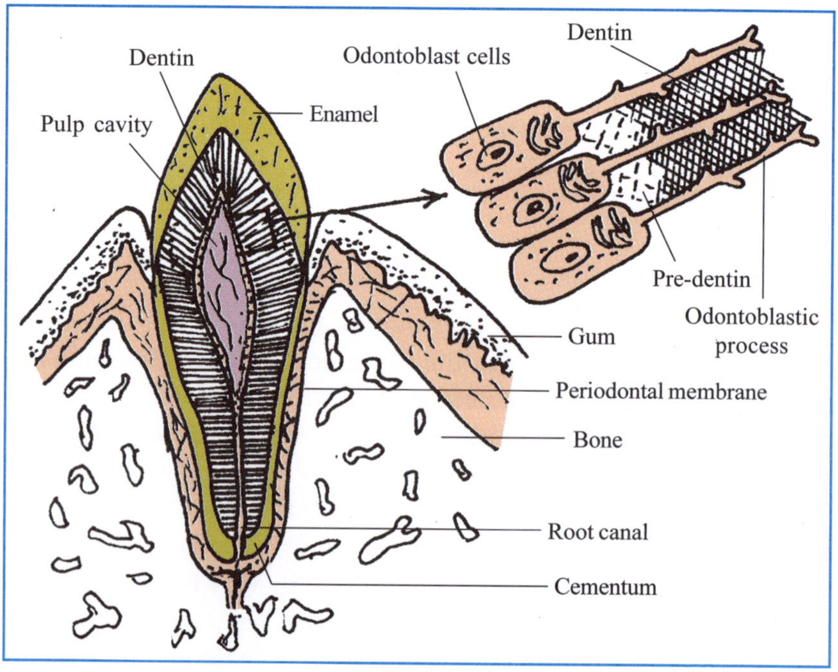

Fig. 5.3 Tooth (longitudinal section).

manner. These processes may sometimes be branched. Around or in between the odontoblastic processes organic intercellular substance is deposited which is composed of reticular and collagenic fibers at first. This uncalcified intercellular substance of dentin subsequently become calcified to form the hard dentin. The recently formed intercellular substance of dentin which is naturally close to the odontoblasts, remain uncalcified for a short period, called **pre-dentin**. Due to the presence of cytoplasmic processes of odontoblast in the dentin, the tooth is very sensitive to stimuli.

Enamel

The projected part of the tooth above the level of gum is known as crown. Crown has an external covering of hard translucent material known as enamel. It is composed of radially arranged hexagonal rods the enamel prisims derived from ***Ameloblast cells***. These enamel prisims are held together by cement substance. Generally each amiloblast cell produces one enamel rod. The enamel is composed mainly of calcium phosphate in the form of apatite $Ca_{10}F_2 (PO_4)_6$ and very small amount of protein and carbohydrate. Enamel is the hardest substance of the body. The enamel once damaged cannot regenerate.

Cementum

The narrow part of the tooth which remains implanted into the alveolar socket is known as root. Cementum is a hard substance which covers the root.

It is slight yellowish is colour and composed of modified bone tissue. The upper part (close to crown) is devoid of cells. Rest part of the cementum has cells in the lacuna, called ***cementoblasts***. The periphery of the cementum contains some bundles of collagen fiber and extend to the bony socket to form ***Periodontal membrane***. This membrane is similar to periosteum, lines the alveolus and attaches the cementum to the alveolar socket.

PHARYNX

This funnel shaped part of G. I. tract is common to digestive and respiratory passages and has three parts – Nasopharynx, Oropharynx and laryngopharynx. The wall of the pharynx is composed of following layers.

(a) Inner mucous coat

Lining epithelium – It is nonkeratinised stratified squamous epithelium in the Ora-pharynx and laryngopharynx and pseudostratified columnar ciliated epithelium in the nasopharynx.

Lamina propria – Other than serous and mucous glands, it contains collections of lymphoid tissue. These are known as pharyngeal tonsils. Such collections of lymphoid tissue at the lateral wall of oropharynx are known as **palatine tonsils**.

(b) Muscular coat

Bundles of ill-defined skeletal muscle fibers are arranged in a thin layer intermingled with fibro elastic connective tissue.

(c) Outer fibrous coat

It is a fibro elastic layer and attaches the pharynx to the surrounding structures.

GENERAL HISTOLOGICAL CHARACTERISTICS OF G. I. TRACT

Form esophagus to rectum of the Gastro-intestinal tract exhibits a common histological feature as follows, with regional variations :

1. Mucous coat

It comprises of a) Lining epithelium, b) Lamina propria and c) Mucularis mucosae.

The ***lining epithelium*** is stratified squamous in the esophagus and in the anal canal. The epithelium of the rest portions of the G.I. tract is of simple columnar type. These columnar cells perform absorptive or secretory functions. Mucus secreting goblet cells remain scattered in the epithelial lining of different parts of G.I. tract. Abrupt transition of the mucosa is present at the gastro-esophageal junction, gastro-duodenal junction, ileo-cecal junction and ano-rectal junction.

The ***lamina propria*** is composed of loose connective tissue, glands, blood vessels and nerves. It supports the lining epithelium. The blood and lymph capillaries those remain close to the epithelial surface and extend into the intestinal villi of small intestine, allow absorption of digested food materials.

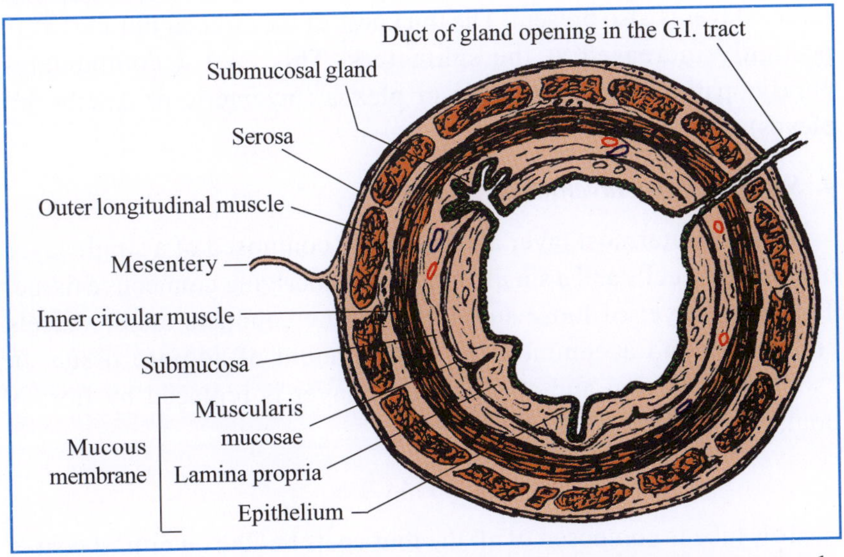

Fig. 5.4 General pattern of histological features of alimentary canal.

The ***muscularis mucosae*** generally very thin and comprises of an outer layer of longitudinal and an inner layer of circular muscle fibers. Some fibers from this layer may extend in to the lamina propria which invaginated into various foldings of mucous membrame or in to the villi. In anal canal it is absent. This layer helps localized movement of the mucous membrane.

2. Submucous coat

It is composed of loose connective tissue with predominance of elastic fibers and contains vessels, nerves, lymphatics and sometimes submucosal glands. They are mainly present in two places – Brunner's glands of duodenum and glands in the lower part of esophagus. This coat connecets the muscular coat with the mucous coat. The nerve fibers and cells form ***Meissner's plexus*** of sub mucosa. Unmyelinated fibers are derived from various plexuses of sympathetic division of ANS and the cell bodies of terminal ganglia of parasympathetic system are mostly derived from vagus nerve.

3. Muscular coat

This is the bulky part of the wall and is composed of inner circular and outer longitudinal muscle fibers. However, in stomach an inner oblique muscle layer is also present. The thickness of the circular muscle fibers is highly increased at the sphincters. This coat accommodates parasympathetic ganglion cells or plexus (myenteric or Auerbach's plexus).

4. Serous coat (Adventitia)

It is the outermost layer and generally composed of a single layer of squamous cells and a small amount of underlying connective tissue. This outer layer of loose supporting tissue conducts major vessels and nerves and accommodates some amount of adipose tissue. In esophagus, rectum and anal canal the layer is replaced by fibrous coat.

ESOPHAGUS

This tube is composed of all the four coats but the outermost coat is fibrous instead of serous.

Mucous coat

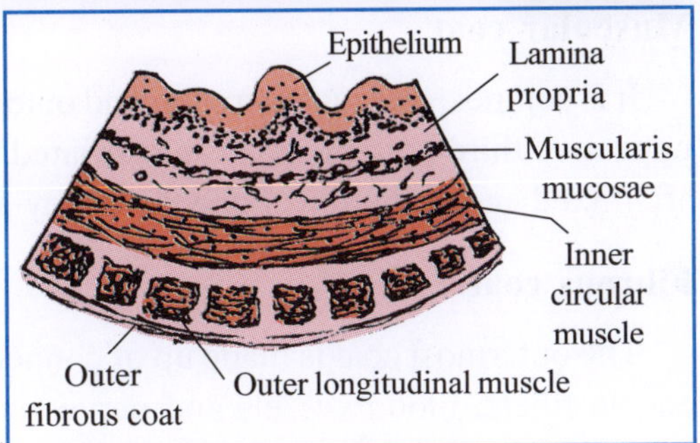

Fig. 5.5 Esophagus (diagramatic).

The *lining epithelium* is made up of non-keratinized stratified squamous epithelium. *Lamina propria* may or may not contain few branched tubular glands. It is made up of fine collagen and elastic fibers. The *muscularis mucosae* is composed of longitudinally arranged smooth muscle fibers. They are indistinct or absent at the cranial part and prominent at the caudal part.

Sub mucous coat

It is composed of loose connective tissue, large vessels and nerves. It contains mucous or seromucous glands at its lower part.

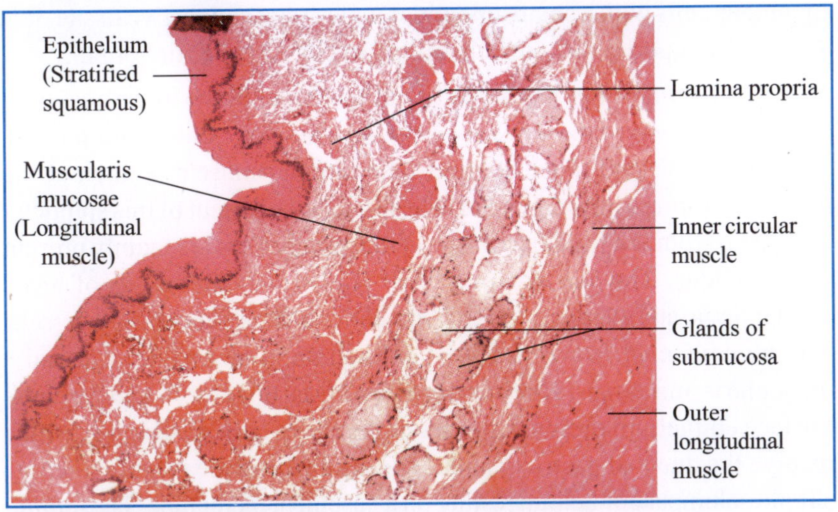

Fig. 5.6 Esophagus – Lower part (Transverse section).

1. The mucous membrane is made up of non-keratinised stratified squamous epithelium ;
2. Muscularis mucosae is prominent ;
3. Submucous coat contains vessels and glands.

Muscular coat

It is composed of inner circular and outer longitudinal muscles. In the upper one third both the layers are striated, in the middle one third they are mixed and in the lower one third they are of smooth variety.

Fibrous coat

The outermost coat is made up of connective tissue containing many elastic fibers, blood vessels and nerves in the cervical region. In the thoracic part the tunica muscularis is invested by mediastinal pleura. The abdominal part is very small and is covered by peritoneum.

STOMACH

This is the dilated part of the G. I. tract and is designed for the breakdown of the food materials to make it suitable for enzymic activity. The wall of the stomach is composed of all the usual layer of the G. I. tract. These are– a) serous coat, b) Muscular coat, c) Sub mucous coat and d) Mucous coat. The ***serous coat*** is made up of a single layer of squamous cells with a small amount of underlying connective tissue. It is derived from peritoneal mesothelium and covers the entire organ.

The ***muscular coat*** has an extra oblique layer at the innermost part. This coat consists of three layers of smooth muscles – outer longitudinal, middle circular and inner oblique. The circular muscle is thick at the pylorus to form pyloric sphincter. The dilator component of this sphincter in derived from longitudinal muscle. Oblique muscles are mainly present in the fundus. The ***sub mucous*** layer is as usual. It consists of loose areolar tissue and contains nerves, lymphatics and plexus of blood vessels. The ***mucous coat*** is composed of epithelium, a lamina propria and a muscularis mucosae. ***Mucous membrane*** is thick soft and velvety. Surface epithelium presents numerous depressions of ***gastric pits*** which receive the ducts of gastric glands. The surface and the pits are lined by simple columnar epithelium resting on a basement membrane. The ***lamina propria*** consists of reticular tissue and contains plexus of vessels, nerves and various types of glands.

The surface epithelium is lined by a single layer of tall columnar cells and secrets mucous. The Goblet cells are absent. When the stomach is empty, it shows numerous longitudinal folds called rugae.

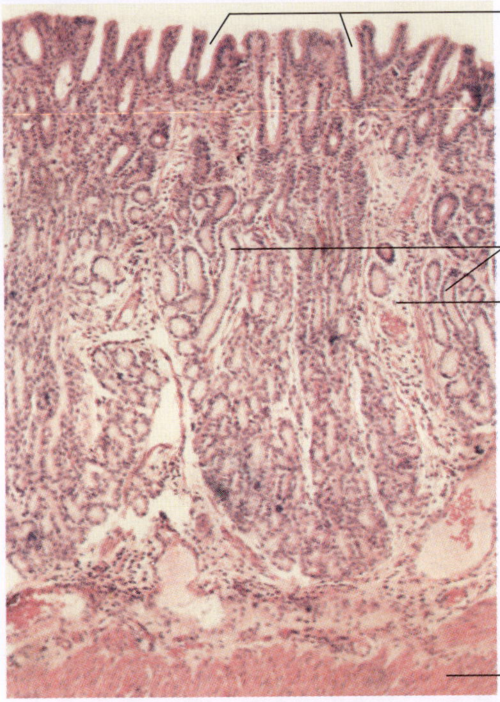

Fig. 5.7 Section of the wall of stomach (fundic part).

1. A number of gastric pits are seen ;
2. Numerous long tubular fundic glands are present ;
3. Lamina propria contains vessels and nerves ;
4. Muscular coat is thick.

The gastric pits in the form of minute depressions give the inner surface of the stomach a honeycomb appearance. The folds become flat when the stomach is filled.

Gastric glands

These are – a) Cardiac glands, b) fundic glands and c) pyloric glands. They are accommodated in the thick mucosa and are bordered at their bases by muscularis mucosa. Actually the epithelium dips into the lamina propria to form long tubular glands. The bases of this invaginated tubes are rounded and appear as acini. These glands open at the depressions on the surface called gastric pits.

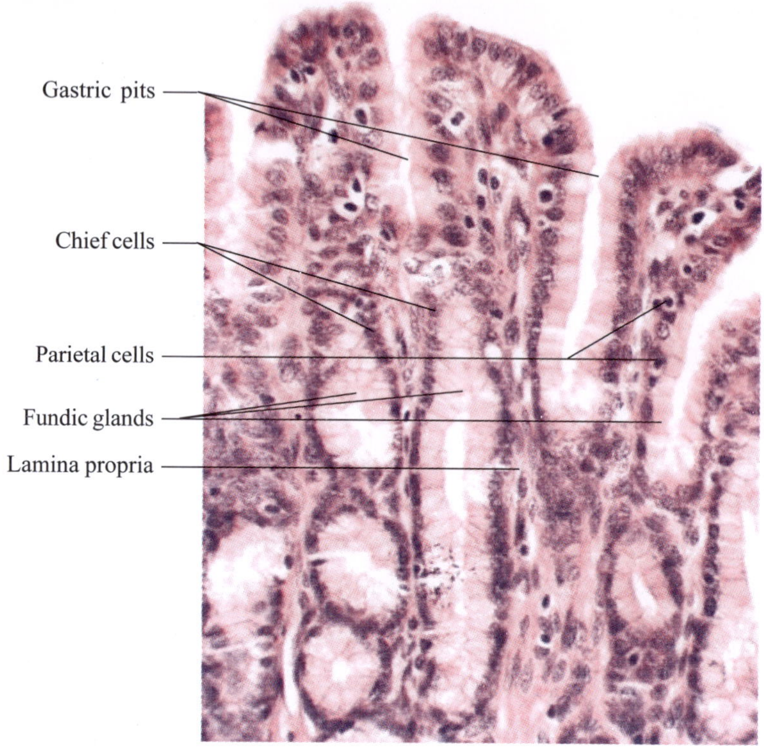

Fig. 5.8 Section of gastric epithelium (higher magnification). (By Courtesy : Dr. Pawan Kumar, Hissar)

1. The surface epithelium is lined by a single layer of tall columnar cells ;
2. Gastric pits, which receive the ducts of the glands are clear ;
3. Chief cells and parietal cells are clearly detected.

Cardiac glands

These glands are situated in the lamina propria of the area around the entrance of the esophagus into the stomach. These are branched tubulo alveolar short mucous glands and composed of the cells of pale cytoplasm. The gastric mucosa is protected from auto-digestion by a thick surface covering of mucus which is maintained at a higher PH than the gastric juice by the secretion of bicarbonate ions from the surface mucous cells.

Fundic glands

These are the main gastric glands and are found in the fundus or body of the stomach. They are simple branched tubular glands with long and straight secreting tubules which open at the bottom of the short gastric pits. Each gland comprises of a blind dilated end called base, a long body and a neck.

The secretory epithelium is composed mainly of four structurally and functionally different types of cells. These are a) ***Chief cells***, b) ***Parietal cells***, c) ***Mucous neck cells*** and d) ***Argentaffin cells***.

CHIEF CELLS (peptic cells or zymogenic cells)

These cells are numerous and are cuboidal, pyramidal or spherical in shape. They are situated at the base and body of the gland and contain zymogen granules in the cytoplasm between the nucleus and free surface. They secret pepsinogen which form pepsin on hydrolysis.

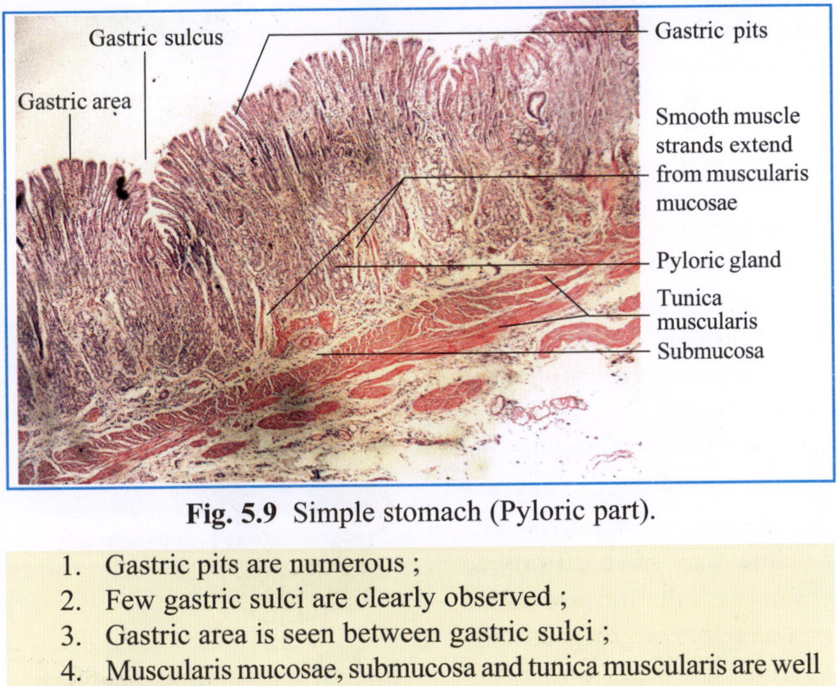

Fig. 5.9 Simple stomach (Pyloric part).

1. Gastric pits are numerous ;
2. Few gastric sulci are clearly observed ;
3. Gastric area is seen between gastric sulci ;
4. Muscularis mucosae, submucosa and tunica muscularis are well marked.

PARIETAL CELLS (oxyntic cells)

They are less in number, large in size and placed between chief cells but pushed towards periphery of the gland. These cells have a spherical nucleus and the cytoplasm stain deeply with Eosin. The cytoplasm contains no secretory granules but possesses numerous mitochondria and microvilli. These cells secrete Hydrochloric acid. A good number of canalicali which are formed due to invagination of cell membrane, end at the lumen of the gland. A number of short microvilli project into the lumen of these canaliculi which greatly increase the surface area.

MUCOUS NECK CELLS

These are large columnar cells mainly situated at the neck of the gland with basal nucleus and pale cytoplasm. They secrete mucous. These cells are considered as stem cells because they divide continuously to replace all other types of cells in the gland.

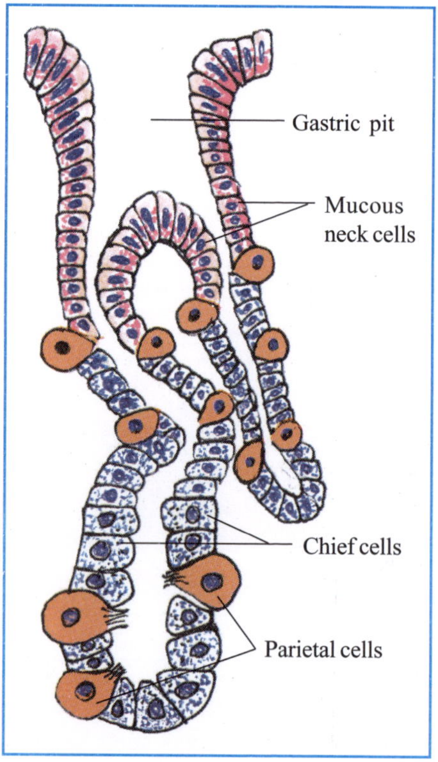

Fig. 5.10 Gastric pit and gland (diagramatic).

ARGENTAFFINE CELLS

These are also less in number and remain interposed between the basement membrane and chief cells. They are demonstrated with silver stain and secrete serotonin which stimulates the muscle to contract. They are called ***entero-chromaffin*** cells because they have affinity to chromium salts and also called ***neuroendocrine*** cells as they secrete serotonin and other hormones.

Pyloric glands

These are simple but branched and coiled, relatively shorter in size and located at the pyloric part of the stomach. The gastric pits are more deeper than those of fundic glands. The cells of these glands are similar to those of mucous neck cells of fundic glands. Some cells of these glands which are present between the mucous cells secrete Gastrin are called G cells. Gastrin stimulates secretion of Hcl in fundic glands. **Gastric sulci** in the form of small permanent furrows are present in the tunica mucosa of this part of stomach. The elevated areas in between these furrows are called **gastric areas**.

Muscularis mucosae : This is a thin layer of smooth muscle. Strands from this muscle extend along the lamina propria of the surface epithelium.

SMALL INTESTINE

The components of small intestine are Duodenum Jejunum and Ileum. There is a general pattern of histomorphological organization because all the components are responsible for absorptive function by enhancing the surface area as well as digestive function by secretion of considerable amount of digestive enzymes from mucosa, submucosa and from glands

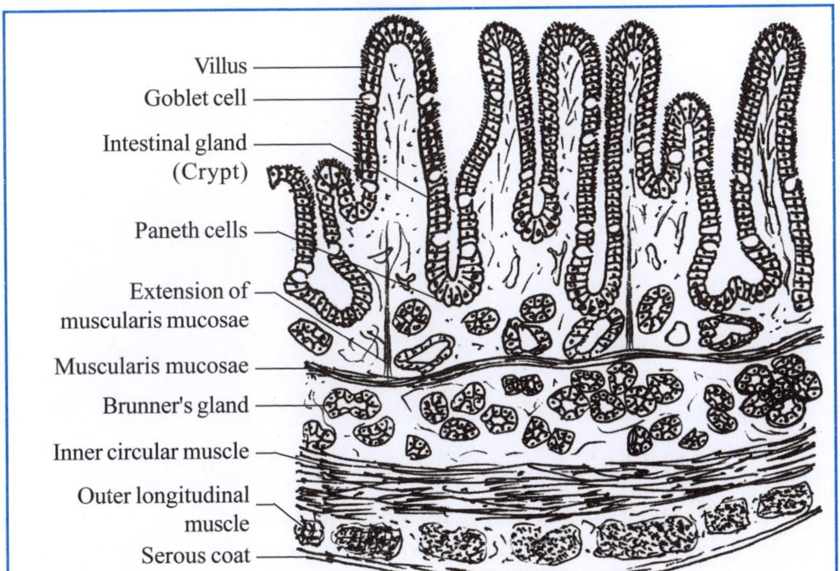

Fig. 5.11 Duodenum, Transverse section (Diagramatic).

out side the intestine. Secretion of mucus for lubrication and protection of living cells from mechanical injury is also another important function.

The common structures of small intestine are mucous, submucous, muscular and serous coats.

Tunica mucosa

Components :

Lining epithelium, lamina propria and lamina musculars (muscularis mucosae).

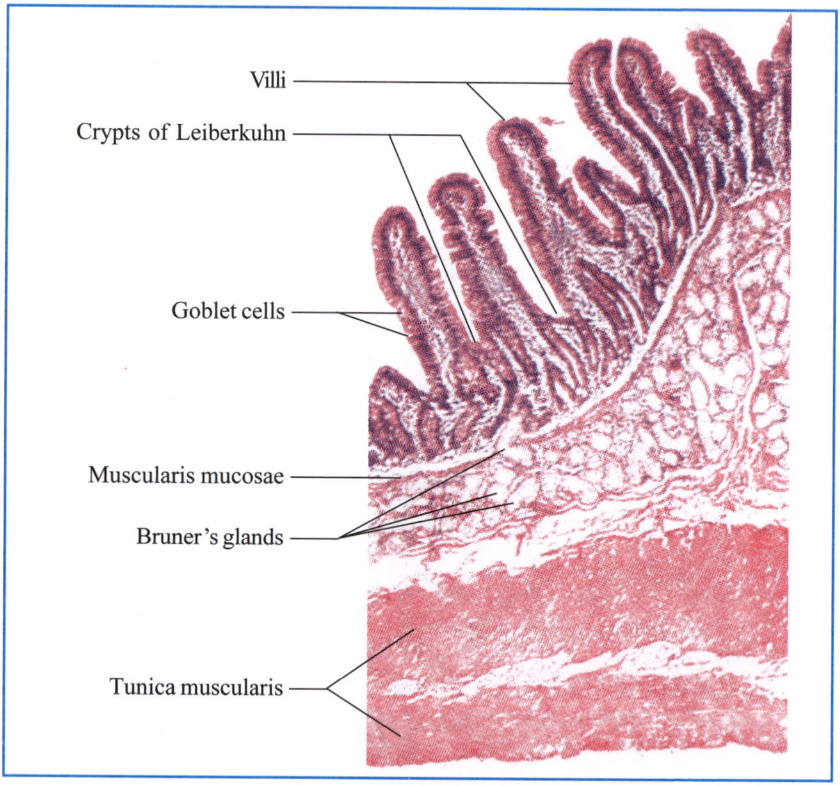

Fig. 5.12 Longitudinal section of duodenum.

1. Villi are arranged in finger like projections ;
2. Crypts of Leiberkuhn are present between bases of the villi ;
3. Bruner's glands are numerous ;
4. Goblet cells are clear.

The ***lining epithelium*** is composed of simple tall columnar epithelium with numerous goblet cells. The surface of the mucosa is studded with finger or leaf like projections which take major part in absorption are called villi.

Villus

This finger like projection is composed of (a) a central blind lymph vessel – the Lacteal, (b) few muscle fibers, (c) plexus of blood vessels and (d) epithelium covering the surface of the villus. They are tongue-like in duoderum, leaf-like in jejunum and finger like in ileum. They are 0.5 to 1 mm long. The epithelium of villi as stated above is made up of tall columnar cells. The free surface of these cells bear tightly packed micro villi which facilitate absorption and give brush border appearance. The cytoplasm is finely granulated. The nucleus is generally oval in shape and situated close to base. The **Goblet cells** (unicellular mucous secreting glands) are sporadically distributed in the epithelium of the villi and glands. The number increases at the distal part of the intestine.

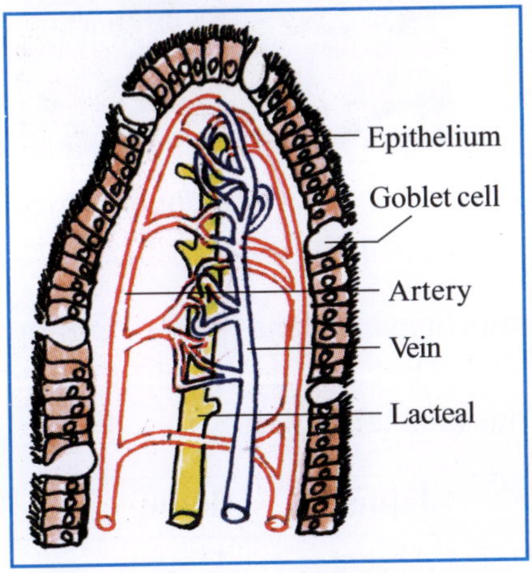

Fig. 5.13 An intestinal villus.

Plica circularis are the circularly disposed mucosal folds which increase the surface area, situated at the upper two third of the small intestine. They are absent in proximal one inch of duoderum and distal six inch in ileum. These folds are meant for increasing surface area for absorption.

Crypts of Lieberkuhn

These are the simple tubular glands which have been formed by the downward extension of the grooves between the bases of the villi up to the lamina muscularis. The lining epithelium is continuous with that of surface but have short micrivilli. Goblet cells are present. Some undifferentiated stem cells are present in the epithelium which proliferate by mitosis to form goblet and columnar cells. These cells are responsible for continuous replacement of the epithelium of small intestine. Some pyramid shaped cells present at the base of the glands called **paneth cells**. These cells contains large acidophilic granules above nucleus and produce digestive enzymes. At the bottom of many glands some secreting cells are found called **argentaffin cells**. They are identified by silver stain only. They contain granules at the subnuclear part.

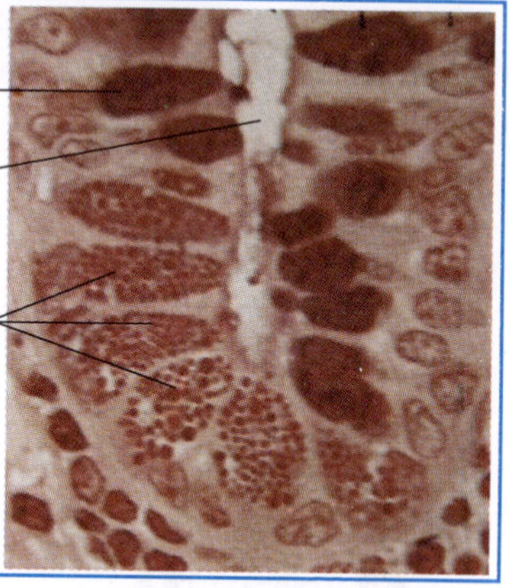

Fig. 5.14 Crypts of Lieberkuhn showing paneth cells.

	Duodenum	**Jejunum**	**Ileum**
Bruner's glands	Most numerous at the proximal part than distal part and absent at the distal end.	Absent	Absent
Villi	Absent in the proximal end. Tongue-like.	Leaf-like	Finger-like
Peyer's patches	Present	Present	More characteristic
Plicae circularis	Glands are found in the core of the plicae	High thin and branching	Decreased in size and number

Lamina Propria

The core of the villi and spaces between the glands are occupied by loose connective tissue. This connective tissue which contains diffuse and solitary lymphoid nodules in places in the lamina propria of small intestine. Externally it is limited by ***lamina muscularis***. This is a thin

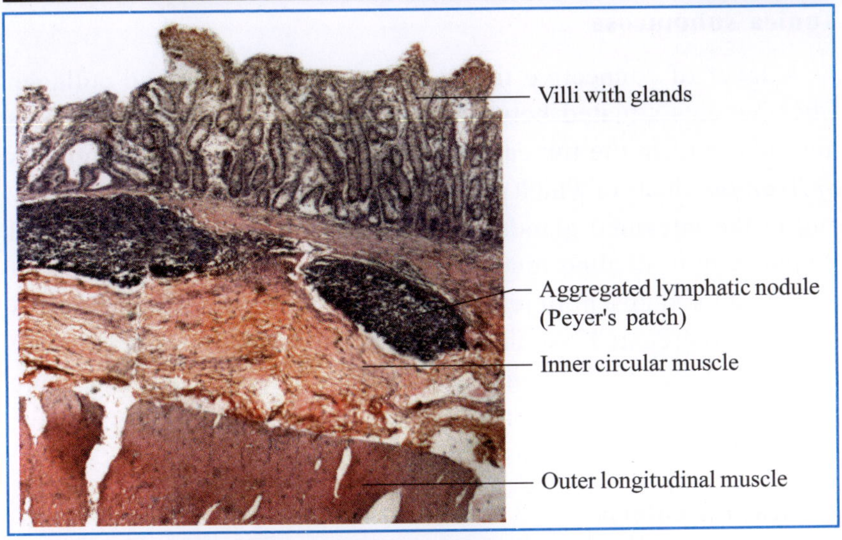

Fig. 5.15 Ileum (Transverse section).

1. The villi are of finger like projections.
2. Short tubular glands are present.
3. Oval or irregular shaped Peyer's patches situated in the submucosa is characteristic.

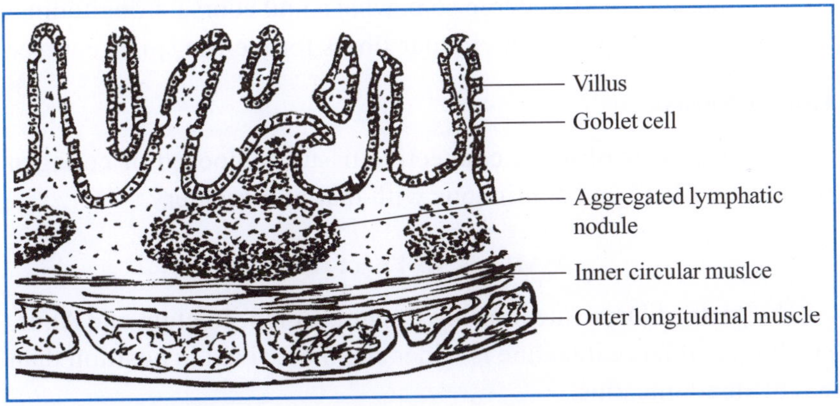

Fig. 5.16 Transverse section of Ileum (diagramatic).

layer of smooth muscle remains after the lamina propria and composed of an inner circular and outer longitudinal fibers. Some of its fibers extend into the villi.

Tunica submucosa

A layer of connective tissue composed of elastic and collagen fiber bundles situated between the lamina muscularis and tunica muscularis form the tunica submucosa. This layer contains ***glands of Brunner***, ducts of which pierce the muscularis mucosae and mostly end in the intestinal glands (crypts of Leiberkuhn). Bruners gland secrete a thin alkaline mucus. These glands are characteristics of duodenum and absent in jejunum and ileum. It also contain ***Peyer's patches*** (aggregated lymph nodules) which are most characteristic in ileum. Along with the glands there are blood vessels and nerve plexuses. The nerve cells of submucous (Meissner's) plexus are post ganglionic neurons of parasympathetic system.

Tunica muscularis

Tunica muscularis is composed of inner circular and outer longitudinal bundles of smooth muscle fibers. Between the two layers, a coarser variety of nerve plexuses are lodged. They contain cell bodies of parasympathetic neurons and fibers of autonomic nervous system and are called Myoenteric (Auerbach's) Plexus. However, both the muscle layers undergo somewhat spiral course. Longitudinal fibers make long spiral and circular fibers form close spiral course.

Tunica Serosa

This is a layer of loose connective tissue composed of collagen and elastic fibers and continuous with that of mesentery.

LARGE INTESTINE

The parts of large intestine are Cecum, Colon, Rectum and Anus. The lumen of large intestine is wider and more fixed in position than that of small intestine.

Common histological features of large intestine :

1. Villi are absent
2. Intestinal glands are more straight, long and compact
3. Paneth cells are absent
4. Goblet cells are numerous

5. Plicae circularis are absent. However 3 or 4 permanent semilunar folds (Houston's Valves) are found in the rectum
6. Lymphatic nodules are numerous
7. Longitudinal mucosal folds are present

Cecum and appendix

It is a dilated and sacculated cul-de-sac presents taeniae (taeniae coli) on its surface and receives the terminal end of ileum. Appendix is a narrow worm like diverticulum from the postero-medial wall of cecum and therefore called vermiform appendix.

With some variations in the appendix and anal canal, rest of the large intestine presents almost common histological structure.

Vermiform Appendix

The outer ***serous coat*** is derived from peritoneum.

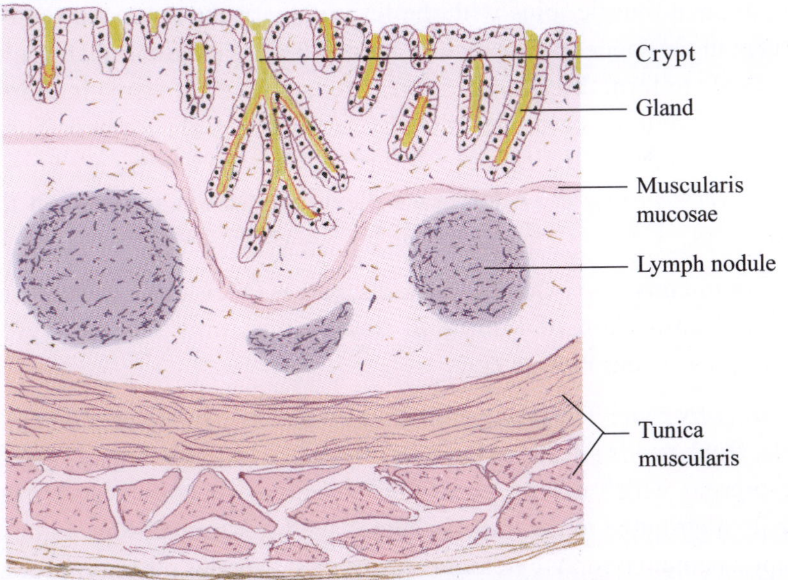

Fig. 5.17 Section of the wall of vermiform appendix (reconstituted).

1. Villi are absent but few pits are seen.
2. Lymph nodules in the submucosa are characteristic.
3. Glands are simple and lined by short columnar cells.

The ***Muscular coat*** is formed by the inner circular and outer longitudinal muscles. These are little thin in some places. The sites where the muscles are deficient, called *hiatus muscularis* through which infection can extend from lumen to the peritoneal surface.

Submucous coat is thick and accommodates large number of masses of lymphoid tissue. Appendix is called abdominal tonsil due to presence of these lymphatic follicles which buldge inside the lumen.

The ***mucous membrane*** in lined by simple columnar cells which also extend into the crypts. These depressions or crypts are also called pits. Numerous goblet cells are found.

Histological structure of colon and rectum

Serous coat : It is derived from peritoneum.

Muscular coat : Inner circular muscle is thick around the upper part of anal canal and forms sphincter ani internus (involuntary). The longitudinal muscle joins with the levator ani at the anorectal region. Except in the appendix and rectum, some fibers of longitudinal muscles aggregate to form three *taeniae coli*. The length of the taenia is shorter than the length of colon and thereby sacculations are formed. These sacculations are called *Haustra*. Folds between the haustra are known as *plicae semilunares*. Auerbach's plexus is present in between the two layers.

Submucous coat : Contains vessels, nerves (Meissner's plexus) and isolated collection of lymphoid tissue containing Lymphocytes, Macrophages and Plasma cells.

Mucous coat : The lining epithelium is made up of simple columnar cells. Goblet cells are numerous. Closely packed straight tubular glands are present which extend up to the muscularis mucosae. Crypts are evenly distributed in the mucous coat. Paneth cells are absent. Lamina propria contain lymphocytes and plasma cells. Venous plexus is present in the lamina propria at the level of ano-rectal junction.

Anus

1. The simple columnar epithelium of rectum and superior part of anal canal changes to stratified squamous non keratinized

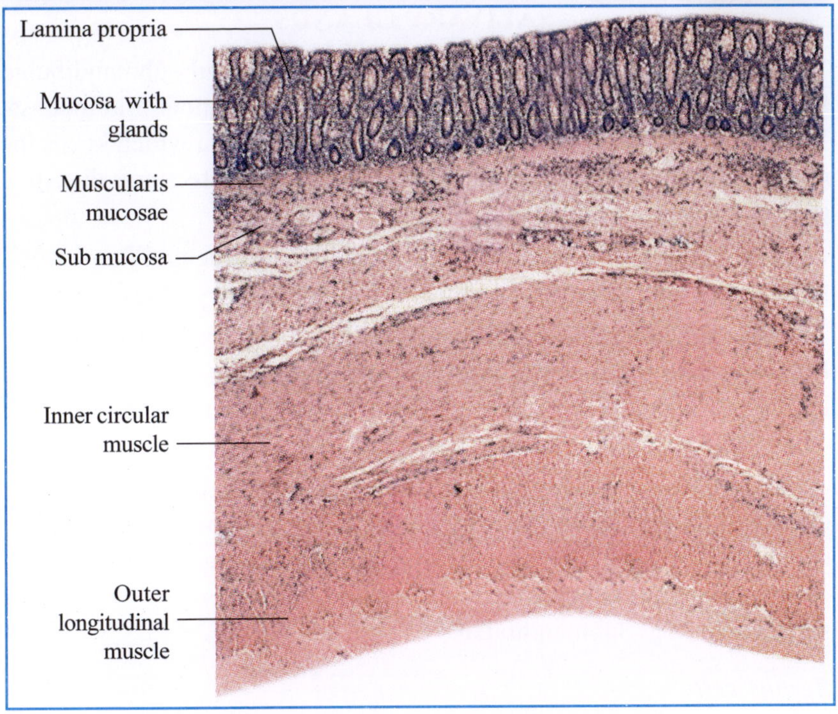

Fig. 5.18 Colon (Longitudinal section).

1. The mucosa is thicker due to closely packed intestinal glands ;
2. Villi are absent and Goblet cells are numerous ;
3. Lymphatic tissue is present in the submucosa.

epithelium abruptly at the distal part. Further distally the epithelium become Keratinised and continuous with the skin.

2. Glands are absent
3. In the columnar zone the depressions between the columns are called sinuses.
4. Sphincter ani ineternus muscle is formed by the inner circular muscle fibers of tunica muscularis and therefore smooth. The external sphincter muscle is striated. Longitudinal muscles which remains between these two layers are smooth and striated.

Digestive system associated Glands

Glands associated with the Digestive system are – **salivary glands**, **liver** and **pancreas**.

SALIVARY GLANDS

Major salivary glands are parotid, sublingual and submandibular. Beside these some minor glands are scattered throughout oral mucosa. These are branched tubuloacinar glands secrete saliva which keeps the mouth cavity moist and lubricated. They also secrete some digestive enzymes and inorganic ions.

All the major salivary glands are similar in their structural frame work. Differences are there in the details of histology and cytology.

Each gland consists of numerous lobules which are held together by fibro-areolar stroma in which nerves and vessels are distributed. Each lobule is composed in succession of secretory end-pieces, intercalated ducts, striated ducts and collecting ducts.

According to the type of secretory cells the salivary glands are classified into (a) serous salivary glands, composed of serous secretory cells e. g parotid. (b) Mucous salivary glands containing mucous secreting cells e. g sublingual. (c) Mixed salivary gland contains both mucous and serous cells, e.g. Submandibular.

Serous cells

Shape – pyramidal

Size – Comparatively small

Nucleus – Round and placed close to the base.

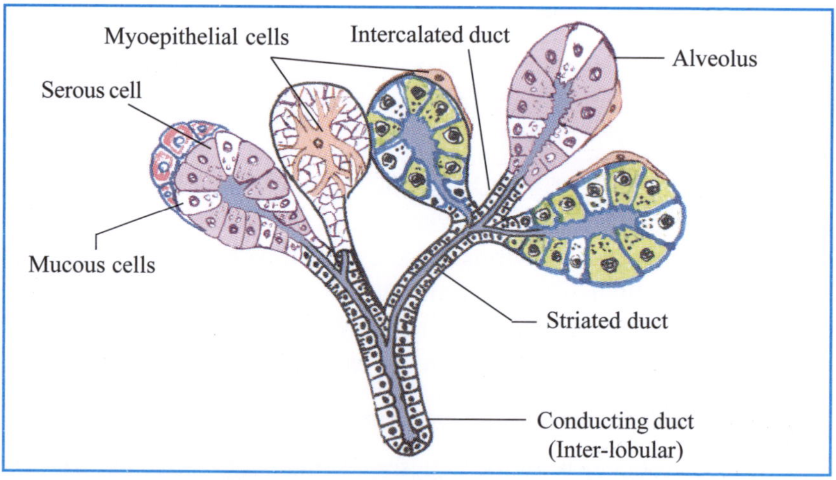

Fig. 5.19 A diagramatic representation of salivary glands.

Cytoplasm – Contains zymogen granules at the supra nuclear part. Basal part take basic stain due to presence of rough E. R.

Myoepithelial cells (basket cells) are spindle shaped cells with many long cytoplasmic processes and located between basal lamina and bases of the secretory cells. These cells contain fibrils and help in expulsion of secretion.

Mucous cells

Shape – polyhedral

Size – Comparatively larger

Nucleus – Flattened and placed close to the base

Cytoplasm – Light staining and foamy in appearance. It contains large granules of mucinogen.

Ducts

The **intercalated ducts** which are lined by a single layer of low cuboidal cells join with the striated ducts which are also intralobular in position. These striated ducts are lined by cuboidal or columnar cell with striations at their bases.

These striated cells play role in transportation of water, ions and excretion of salts. These ducts join with the inter-lobular duct at the septa which are also lined by simple columnar epitherium. The lining cells are not striated and changes to stratified columnar when they join with similar ducts. Further union of such ducts leads to the formation of main parotid duct which opens in the mouth where it is lined by stratified squamous epithelium.

Parotid salivary gland

This ***serous*** tubuloacinar salivary gland is enveloped by connective tissue capsule from which septa enter inside the gland and divide the parenchyma into numerous lobules. These lobules accommodate a number of alveoli or acini of various shape and sizes, small ducts, blood vessels and nerves.

Parenchyma

It is composed of closely packed acini which are lined by single layer of serous cells. However this gland also have sero-mucous

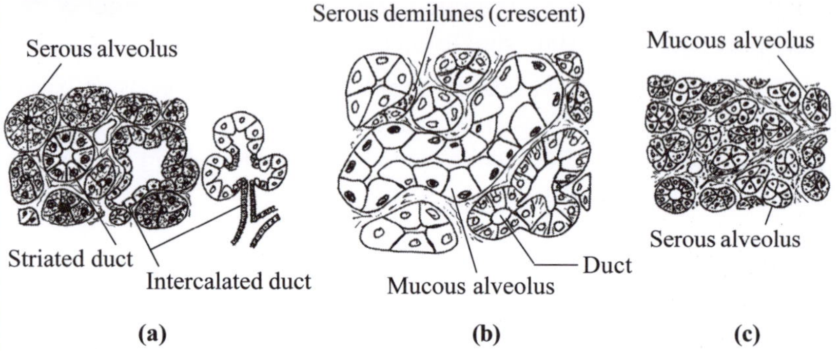

Fig. 5.20 (a) Serous salivary gland; (b) Mucous salivary gland; (c) Mixed salivary gland.

acini. The lumen of an acinus is small or sometimes obliterated and open into short **intercalated duct**. These ducts are lined by low cuboidal epithelium.

Sublingual salivary gland

It is a branched tubuloacinar gland, and is of mucous variety, but seromucous cells are also presnet. The capsule of the gland is not distinct

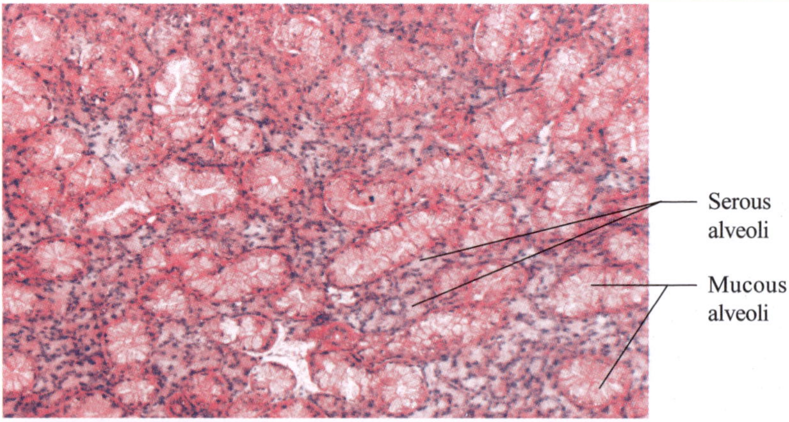

Fig. 5.21 Salivary gland. Mixed type (Submandibular).

1. Both serous (white) and mucous (dark) ascini are visible ;
2. Few intercalated and some striated ducts are also observed ;
3. Connective tissue is plenty in between ascini.

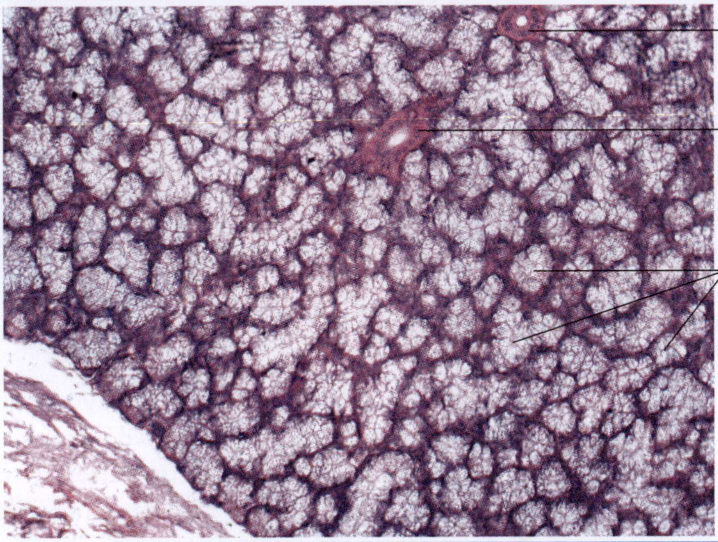

Fig. 5.22 Salivary gland ; Mucous type (Sublingual).

1. Ascini are numerous and predominantly of mucous type ;
2. Few large and small ducts (striated and inter-lobular) are observed ;
3. Lumen of ascini and intercalated ducts are also visible.

but connective tissue septa are well developed. Terminal alveoli are mostly elongated and often open directly in the larger intra lobular duct. The acini are foamy in appearance.

Submandibular salivary gland

It is a compound branched tubuloacinar gland of ***mixed type***. The connective tissue frame work is similar to that of parotid. Some alveoli are completely serous and some are purely mucous with prominent lumen. However some alveoli contains both serous and mucous cells. Some other mucous alveoli have serous crescents associated with them. These crescent or half-moon shaped clusters of cells are called ***serous demilunes***. Duct system is similar to that of parotid. Secretory activities are controlled by ANS. Parasympathetic nerve fibers (secreto motor) of Facial and Glossopharyngeal and sympathetic nerve fibers from superior cervical ganglion supply these glands.

LIVER

It is the largest gland in the body which parforms multiple complex functions. Beside production of bile, liver is involved in metabolism of nutritional substances, viz. , fat, protein, carbohydrate, vitamins and minerals. It is also associated with synthesis of various proteins, phagocytosis and detoxification. This solid gland is composed of several lobes. Each lobe comprises of numerous small lobules. The whole of the gland is covered by a connective tissue sheath is called Glisson's capsule. This fibrous capsule enter the gland and form incomplete septa between the lobules.

The parenchyma cells of the liver, the hepatocytes undergo rapid mitosis when part of the organ is removed, until the original volume is restored within few weeks. This is one of the characteristic feature of the organ and surgical removal of 2/3rd of the liver may be compatible to life.

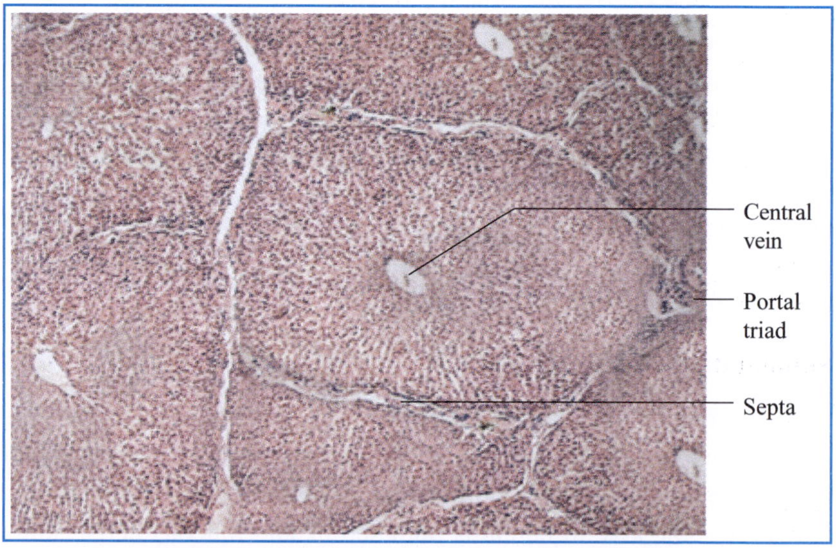

Fig. 5.23 Section of liver (low magnification).

1. Hepatic lobules are surrounded by very thin connective tissue ;
2. Central vein is large ;
3. Hepatic cords and sinusoids are clear ;
4. Portal triad contains minute branches of artery, portal vein and bile duct.

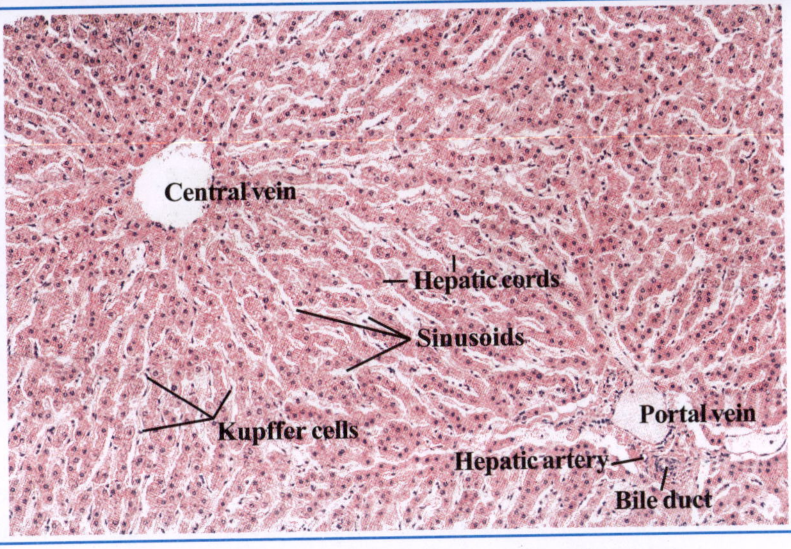

Fig. 5.24 Hepatic lobule (higher magnification).

Liver cells

The hepatocytes are polyhedral cells with large round nucleus and prominent nucleolus. These cells are arranged in the form of plates with single cell thickness. The shape and sizes of the liver cells depends on the location. Due to such disposition these cells have few contact surfaces and some free surfaces. With the contact surfaces they are attached to the adjoining cells by zona occludens (tight junction) and macula adherences (desmosomes) and the free or exposed (sinusoidal) surfaces are studded with short broad microvilli.

Beside the hepatocytes there are specialized macrophages, called ***Kupffer's cells*** and few endothelial cells.

Hepatic lobules

Each lobule having an approximate length of 2 mm and a diameter of 1 mm. Each of them is surrounded by connective tissue septa. This is prominent in the liver of pig. The center of the lobule is occupied by the ***central vein*** along the axis from which the hepatocytes in the form of cords or plates are arranged in a radiating

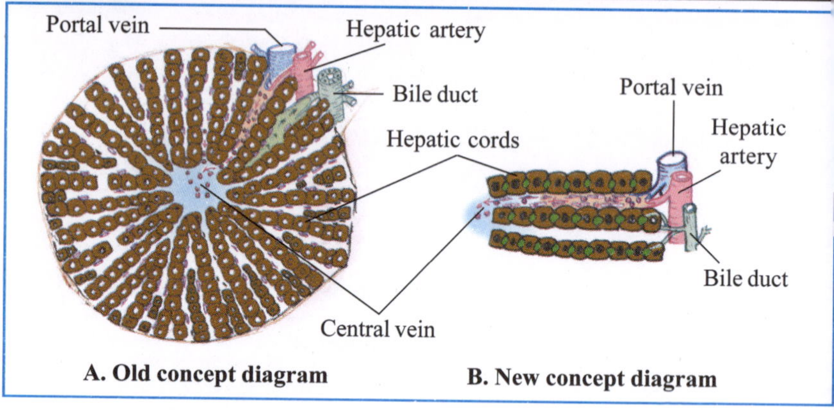

Fig. 5.25 Schematic diagram of a hepatic lobule.

manner towards periphery. The spaces in between the plates (laminae) are called ***sinusoids***. The small triangular space between adjoining three such lobule accommodates branches of hepatic artery, portal vein and bile duct and are collectively known as ***Portal triad***. The radiating plates of hepatocytes has, on one side a bile capillary going out of the lobule to join larger ducts at the portal triad and on the other side, a vascular capillary towards the center to join with the central vein.

But as per current concept, the bile canaliculi start as a space between the two hepatocytes (Fig. 5.25B) of hepatic lamina. Although the cell membrane of hepatocytes form the wall of these canaliculi at the beginning but ultimately they get their own wall and form bile ductules at the portal triad.

Portal lobule

In this concept the portal lobule is demarcated between three adjacent central veins around a portal triad. This area is drained by interlobular duct and supplied by interlobular branch of portal vein. The flow of blood in this area is opposite to that of bile and lymph.

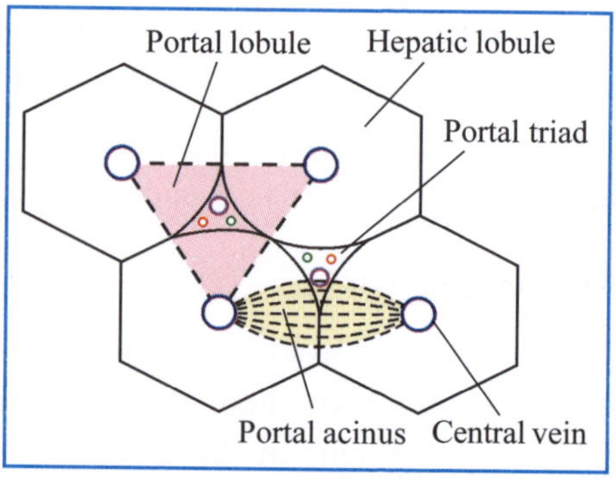

Fig. 5.26 Diagramatic representation of various types of lobules.

Portal acinus

This is a spindle shaped area of the hepatic parenchyma between two adjacent central veins which is supplied by a preterminal branch of an hepatic arteriole. This is considered on the basis of pattern of oxygenation and pathological degeneration.

Hepatic laminae

The one cell thick radiating irregular branching and anastomosing plates formed by the hepatocytes are called hepatic laminae. The adjoining laminae are interconnected by bridges of liver cells. Presence of perforations at the laminae make an intercommunating system between adjacent sinusoids.

Hepatic sinusoids

These are the spaces between the hepatic laminae which anastomose with each other by perforations. These sinusoids are lined by endothelial cells and **Kupffer's cells**. The Kupffer's cells are large, having processes and are phagocytic in nature. They also help in formation of bile pigments. There is a space between the sinusoid and hepatic laminae called perisinusoidal space or ***space of Disse***. These spaces are filled with blood plasma and chylomicrons which percolate through the fenestrated walls of sinusoids and contain, in addition, ***Ito cells***. Liver cells convert chylomicrons into Lipoproteins. Ito cells secrete collagenous matrix including proteoglycans and provide growth factor for regeneration of damaged liver cells. They also store fat soluble vitamin A in lipid vesicles.

Biliary apparatus

It consists of biliary duct and gall bladder. These structures carry bile, store it and expel to the intestine at the time of need.

Bile duct

The biliary passage starts with bile canaliculi (sinusoid) which empty into interlobular ductules and then to wider ducts. The intrahepatic ducts are lined by culoidal cells and the extra hepatic ducts are lined by columnar cells. All these cells have striated borders due to presence of microvilli.

Occasionally small mucous glands are present in the submucosa which open into the depression of the mucous membrane. Externally these ducts have a fibro elastic coat with some smooth muscle fibers.

Extra hepatic part consists of common hepatic duct, gall bladder cystic duct and common bile duct.

Gall Bladder

This is a small pear shaped sac situated at the undersurface of the right part of liver, close to the right end of porta hepatic and joins with the common hepatic duct via cystic duct.

The wall of the gall bladder in made up of a serous coat, muscular coat and mucous coat. ***The serous*** coat is derived from peritonium and is incomplete. The fibers of the ***muscular coat*** is irregularly disposed However, longitudinal fibers are prominent. A fibro-elastic coat supports the muscular coat.

In the ***mucous coat***, muscularis mucosae is absent. The mucous membrane is thrown into a number of folds; hence the interior is honey-comb in appearance. The surface epithelium is made up of a single layer of columnar cells. Three types of cells – tall columnar,

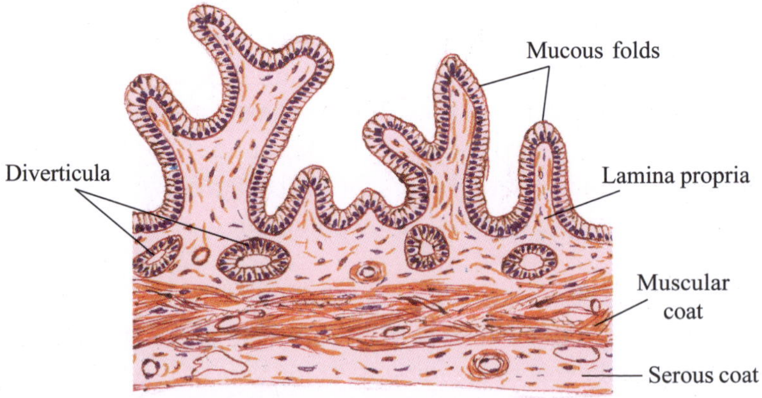

Fig. 5.27 Section of the wall of gall bladder (reconstituted).

1. Mucous membrane is thrown into irregular folds and lined by columnar cells ;
2. Fibers of muscular coat are irregularly disposed ;
3. Muscularis mucosae is absent.

basal cells and pencil cells are found. Microvilli are present on the free surface of the columnar cells. Except the neck region, the lamina propria is devoid of any gland. Few mucous glands are found in the neck.

A number of cresentic valves (spiral valve of Heister) are present in the interior of cystic duct.

Function of Gall bladder

1) It stores as well as concentrates the bile
2) It reduces alkalinity of bile
3) It contracts and releases the bile by the relaxation of sphincter of the neck (sphincter of Oddi) when food reaches the duodenum.

PANCREAS

It is a compound tubulo-acinar gland and has an exocrine and an endocrine portions. The exocrine part produces digestive enzymes which helps in the digestion of carbohydrate, protein and fat. The endocrine portions produce insulin and glucagon, the hormones responsible for regulation of carbohydrate metabolism in the body.

The whole of the gland is covered by a thin connective tissue capsule from which septa pass inside and divide it into a number of lobules. Each lobule consists of ultimate remification of main duct ending in numerous alveoli. Lobules contain numerous alveoli and interacinous cell islets. This lobular arrangement is better developed in the pancreas of cat.

Exocrine part

This is composed of alveoli or acini and their ducts. The acini are lined by a single layer of serous cells with broad bases and narrow apices. The apex is directed towards the lumen and contains numerous course zymogen granules. The basal

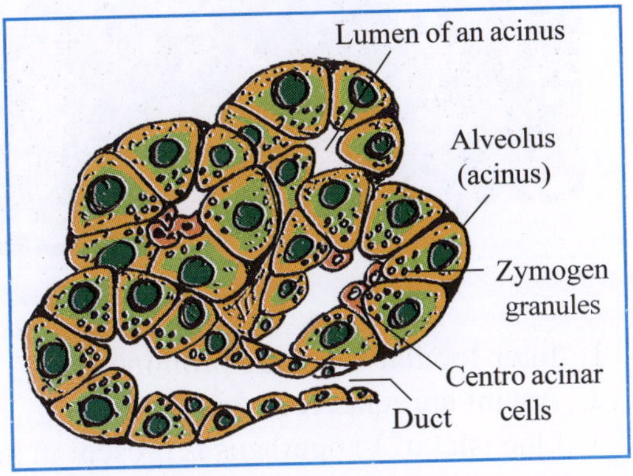

Fig. 5.28 Pancreas (exocrine part).

portion contains round nucleus and is basophilic due to presence of granular endoplasmic reticulum (rER). In some acini one or more cuboidal cells remain in contact with the apices of the secreting cells are called ***centro-acinar*** cells. These cells do not have secretion granules and are continuous with the epithelium of intercalated ducts. The cells of the intercalated ducts secrete a large volume of fluid, rich in bicarbonate ions. The pancreatic cells produce amylase, lipase, trypsinogen, chymotrypsinogen, ribonuclease, deoxyribonuclease and sodium bicarbonate.

The ducts are intercalated and intra lobular but are less in number in comparison to salivary glands. These ducts are long and branch many times before entering the acini. Numerous intra-lobular ducts join to form inter-lobar ducts. The wall of the larger ducts contains elastic fibers and muscles and thereby control flow of pancreatic juice into duodenum.

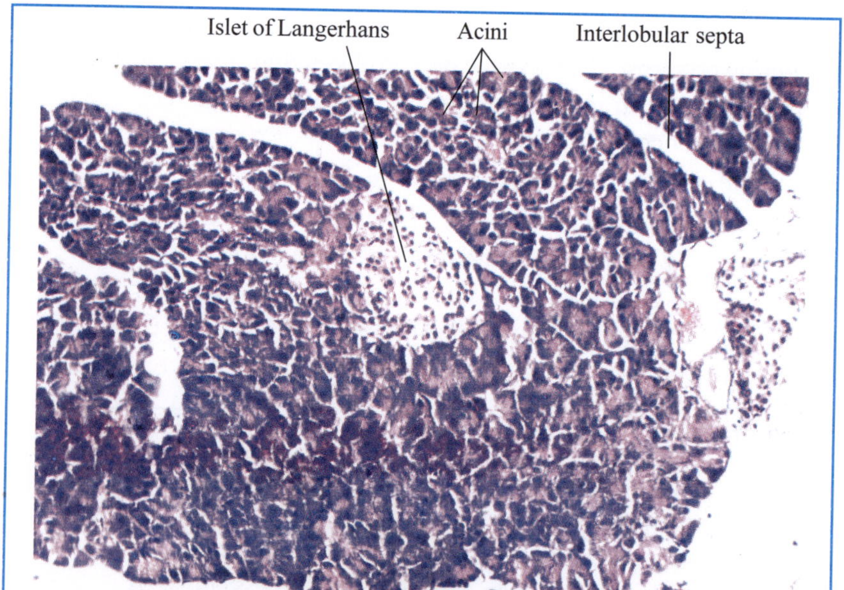

Fig. 5.29 Pancreas.

1. Inter-lobular septa are prominent ;
2. Ascini are numerous and compact ;
3. One islet of Langerhans is present in the form of a lightly stained area.

Endocrine part

Within the exocrine part and in between the acini some roughly spherical light stained cell islets of varying sizes are found. These are called **islets of Langerhans**. These are composed of irregular cords of cells, numerous blood capillaries and few fine connective tissue fibers. By special staining three types of cells can be distinguished. These are α cells, β cells and δ cells. ***α (alpha)*** cells contain numerous fine red coloured granules and secrete glucogon. The cells have distinct membrane. The ***β (beta)*** cells contin coarse dark blue coloured granules and secrete insulin. The membrane of these cells are indistinct. The ***δ (delta)*** cells are few in number and secrete somatostatin, which regulates insulin and glucagon secretion.

All these cells are smaller than the acinar cells. The α cells are generally peripherally placed and β cells are centrally situated. Some other minor cell types are also found in these islets. These are ***PP Cells*** – secrete pancreatic polypeptide hormone which stimulates the secretion of gastric and intestinal enzymes and inhibits motility. ***DI Cells*** – secrete vasoactive intestinal polypeptide (VIP) which induces glycogenolysis and hyperglycemia. ***Enterochromaffin Cells*** – secrete serotonin.

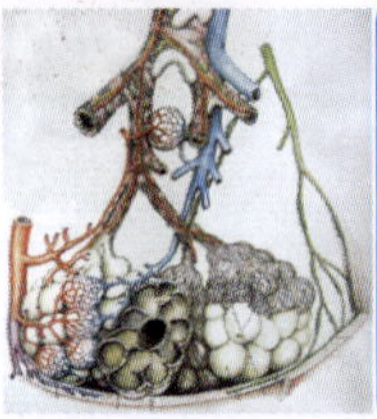

6

RESPIRATORY SYSTEM

Components :

1. Nasal cavity
2. Pharynx
3. Larynx
4. Trachea
5. Lung

NASAL CAVITY

The nasal cavities (left & right) which are separated by osseo-cartilaginous partition extends from mostrils to choanae. These cavities are formed by cartilages and bones and are lined by mucous membrane. There are three parts in this structure– a) Vestibular part, b) Respiratory part and c) Olfactory part.

Vestibular part

The outer portion is similar to epidermis. Hair follicles, Sebaceous and sweat glands are present. The next portion is called transitional zone, which is lined by stratified squamous epithelium. Occasionally serous and seromucous glands are present in the propria submucosa. Plenty of superficial capillary network are found to be connected to larger vessels at the depth of propria submucosa.

Respiratory part

This is lined by pseudo-stratified columnar ciliated epithelium with goblet cells. Plenty of blood vessels, serous and mucous glands are present in the sub-epithelial tissue. The paranasal sinases are lined by simple (squamous/cuboidal) or transitional epithelium or sometimes by columnar ciliated epithelium with few goblet cells. The sub-epithelial connective tissue contains collagen and elastic fibers. The mucus secretion of this epithelium by the goblet cells and mucous gland is sticky and arrest inhaled particles and micro-organisms and act as a natural defence mechanism.

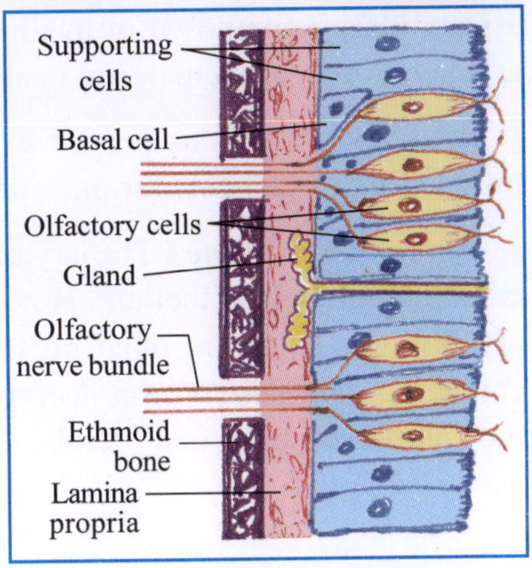

Fig. 6.1 Nasal mucosa – olfactory part (schematic).

Olfactory part

This is the region of ethmoturbinate, part of the dorsal turbinate and nasal septum. It forms posterior ¼th part of nasal cavity. It is lined by neuro-epithelium which contains olfactory, supporting and basal cells. The olfactory cells are modified bipolar neurons and their axons form the bundles of olfactory nerves. Dendrites are distributed on the epithelium and serve as receptors. The supporting cells are columnar type and the basal cells are small cuboidal cells. Tubulo alveolar olfactory glands are present in the lamina propria.

Paranasal Sinuses

These are spaces around the nasal cavity formed as diverticula by invading the neighbouring bones. These spaces contain air and lined by ciliated columnar epithelium.

Pharynx

See digestive system.

Larynx

The components are –

a) Cartilages (Thyroid, cricoids, arytenoids and epiglottis)

b) Muscles

c) Mucous membrane

Cartilages – The epiglottis is a leaf like structure and composed of a central core of clastic cartilage and covered by mucous membrane on both surfaces. Other cartilages – cricoid, thyroid and basal part of arytenoids are composed of hyaline cartilaginous tissue. The apex of arytenoids and corniculate are made up of elastic cartilage.

Muscles – The muscles are extrinsic and intrinsic. The intrinsic muscles are responsible for movement and skeletal in nature.

Mucous membrane – The larynx is mostly lined by pseudo-stratified columnar ciliated epithelium. However, the epiglottis, vocal folds and aryepiglottic folds are lined by stratified squamous non-keratinised epithelium. The lamina propria accommodates mucous and mixed sero-mucous glands and blood vessels.

TRACHEA

This flexible tube is composed of fibro elastic connective tissue and cartilages.

A variable number (16 to 20) of incomplete cartilaginous rings unite one after another to make this tubular air passage. The ends of cartilages are interconnected by elastic fibers and bundles of smooth muscle fibers called Trachealis muscles. The rings are made up of hyaline cartilage.

Externally the wind pipe is covered by a outer fibrous coat which is composed mainly of elastic fibers and contains nerves and vessels.

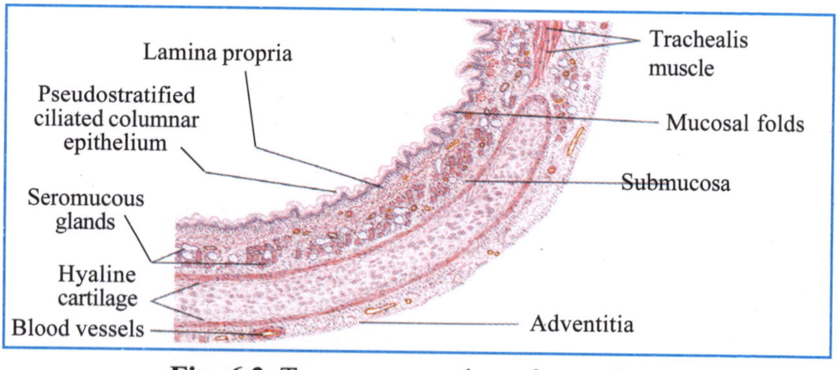

Fig. 6.2 Transverse section of a trachea.

1. The tracheal cartilage/ring is hyaline in nature ;
2. Mucous membrane is lined by ciliated pseudo-stratified columnar epithelium ;
3. Trachealis muscle (smooth) is attached to the end of the cartilage.

The inner mucous coat is composed of a lining epithelium and lamina propria. The lining membrane is made up of Pseudo-stratified columnar ciliated epithelium with numerous goblet cells. The lamina propria contains plenty of elastic fibers, glands (mucous, serous and mixed) and vessels.

The structure of Principal bronchi are similar to that of trachea. However they are smaller in size but the lumen is almost circuler. The cartilaginous rings are complete near bifurcation of trachea. With the subsequent branchings of the air passage the cartilaginous rings are transformed to plates. The passages supported by cartilage are called ***bronchi***. Such passages which are not supported by cartilages are called ***bronchioles***. In the bronchi the mucous membrane is thrown into longitudinal folds during expiration. Discontinuous layer of smooth muscle is present in the mucosa.

The bronchial tree

In the branching arrangement, two principal bronchi presents a definite pattern. The sequence of the branching is as follows :

1. Principal bronchus (Primary)
2. Lobar bronchus (secondary)
3. Segmental bronchus (Tertiry) – several order of branches lead to terminal branchings
4. Terminal branchus
5. Bronchioles – several order of branches lead to terminal bronchioles
6. Terminal bronchiole – subdivides into one to three generations to form respiratory bronchioles
7. Respiratory bronchiole
8. Alveolar ducts
9. Atria
10. Alveolar sacs
11. Alveolus

Broncho pulmonary segment

Each segmental braonchus remifies within a self contained functionally independent units of lung tissue. Therefore a segmental bronchus along with its associated lung parenchyma is called broncho pulmonary segmement.

LUNGS

The lobes of the lungs are enclosed by a serous coat – the pulmonary pleura. Benealth the serous coat a subserous coat is present which is composed mainly of elastic fibers. The lung parenchyma is composed of finer branches of bronchial tree which end into a number of alveoli, blood vessels, lymphatics and nerves.

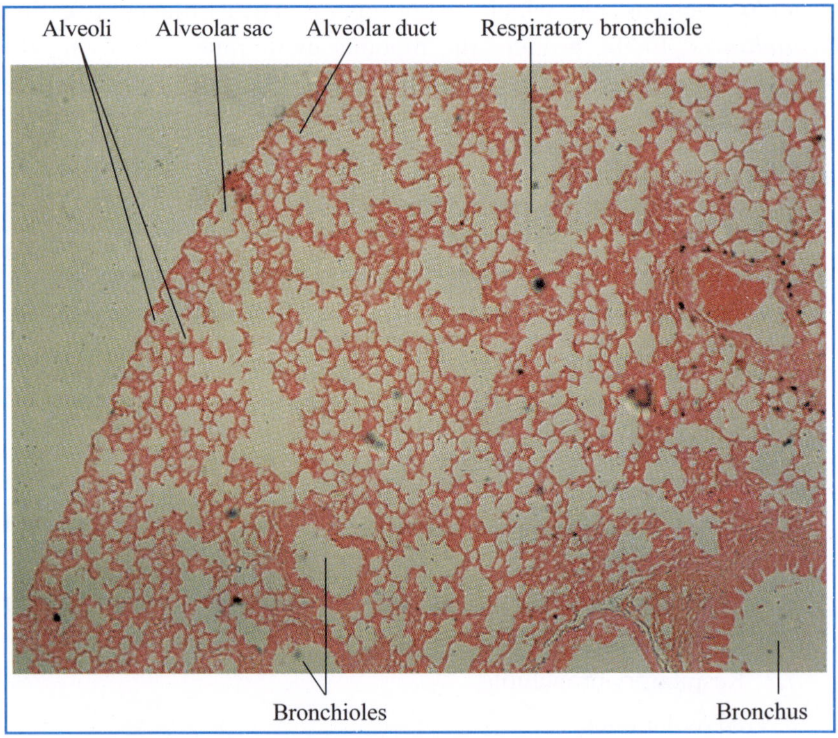

Fig. 6.3 Section of a lung. (By Courtesy : Dr. M. Sinha)

1. Alveoli are in the form of tiny spaces and are lined by simple squamous epithelium ;
2. Alveolar ducts join together to form respiratory bronchiole ;
3. The bronchus appears to be round with folded mucous membrane ;
4. Pulmonary vessels are prominent.

Under microscope the lung tissue shows numerous alveoli in the form of empty spaces surrounded by thin walls, various branches of air passage and blood vessels.

Structure of bronchi (Primary, secondary and Tertiary)

a) The lumen is almost circular.

b) It is lined by pseudo-stratified columnar ciliated epithelium with goblet cells. In the tracho-bronchial passage, ten types of epithelial cells have been detected under EM. Out of these, some important cells are goblet cells, serous cells, cilited cells, clara cells, argentaffin cells, etc.

c) The lamina propria contains smooth muscles arranged in spiral manner along the length.

The mucosa in thrown into longitudinal folds due to muscular contraction. Spasmadic contraction of bronchial muscles constrict the bronchi which leads to difficulty in breathing during asthma. The lamina propria contains mucous and seromucous glands.

d) Cartilagenous plates (hyaline) are arranged in series but in an irregular and overlapping manner.

Structure of bronchioles/terminal bronchioles/Respiratory bronchioles

a) Diameter of these air passages is about 1 mm.

b) They are lined by simple columnar ciliated epithelium. Goblet cells are very few in number.

c) Cartilages, glands and lymphoid tissue are absent.

d) Walls are mainly made up of smooth muscles and elastic fibers.

A small portion of lung tissue ventilated by one bronchiole is called **lobule**.

e) The respiratory bronchioles are generally 0.5 mm in diameter. Their lining epithelium changes to simple cuboidal noncialiated type. Goblet cells are absent. A number of single alveoli protrude out from their walls.

Structure of alveolar duct/atria/alveolar sacs

The alveolar ducts arise from the respiratory bronchioles. They are thin walled and studded with alveolar sacs as well as alveoli. The wall is composed of smooth muscle fibers and elastic fibers and lined by simple squamous epithelium. The alveolar ducts lead to the formation of alveolar sacs from a common space known as atrium. The alveolar sacs give rise to a number of alveoli. The wall of the atrium and sacs are not supported by smooth muscle and therefore composed of elastic fibers and lined by simple squamous epithelium.

Structure of alveoli

These are closely packed tiny spaces and are the ultimate subdivisions of the bronchial tree. Alveoli are lined by a layer of simple squamous epithelium. Since they are tightly packed with the adjacent alveoli, no separate wall of an individual alveolus is formed. Therefore an interalveolar septa is available which contains — (a) alveolar epithelium (***Pneumocyte-I***), (b) reticular and elastic fibers, (c) Blood capillaries, (d) septal cells (***Pneumocyte-II***) and (e) ***Alveolar phagocytes***. However the adjacent alveoli are connected by some minute alveolar pores. So the **blood air barrier** is formed by the alveolar epithelium along with its basal lamina and capillary endothelium.

The Pneumocyte-II cells are large cuboidal cells with micro villi at their free surfaces. These cells Secrets a fluid known as ***surfactant***. This fluid contains phospholipids which reduces surface tension within the alveoli and helps in keeping the alveoli open and prevent them from collapsing. The alveolar phagocytes remain within the septa or in free form inside the alveoli. They are responsible for removing dust and carbon particles which enter the lung during inspiration.

Other components of lung parenchyma are nerve fibers (sympathetic and parasympathetic), pulmonary and bronchial vessels and lymphatics. However lymphatics are absent in atria, alveolar sac and alveoli.

7
URINARY SYSTEM

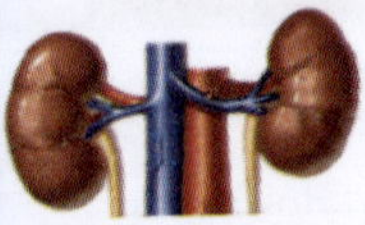

STRUCTURE OF URINARY SYSTEM

Components :

2 Kidneys

2 Ureters

Urinary bladder

Urethra

KINDEYS

These are a pair of reddish-brown roughly bean shaped organs situated one on each side of the vertebral column at the posterior part of the abdomen. They are retroperitoneal in position, invested by a thin capsule and remain surrounded by adipose tissue.

When cut longitudinally, this organ exhibits two distinct zones – a dark peripheral portion, the ***cortex*** and lighter zone with parallel streaks, the ***medulla***. The medulla forms conical structures with the apexes directed inwards and base attached to cortex known as ***Pyramids***. The number of pyramids varies from 8-18.

In warm-blooded animals the kidney is composed of several individual lobes which may remain independently or may fuse partially or completely, depending upon species. In birds and dolphins the lobes are numerous mostly separated. In cattle and in human new born, fusion at the cortex is partial but medulla remains fused.

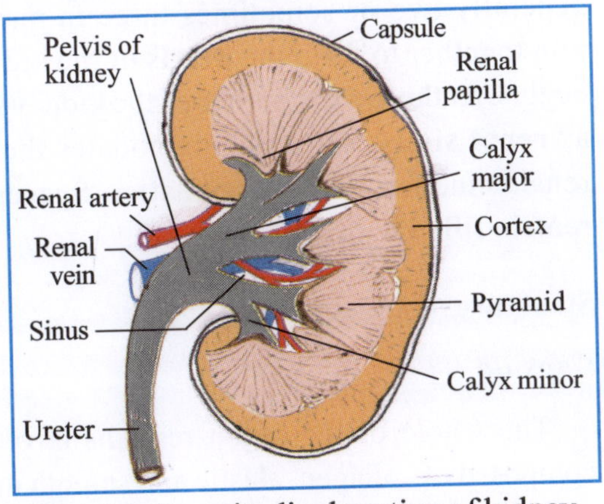

Fig. 7.1 Longitudinal section of kidney (diagramatic).

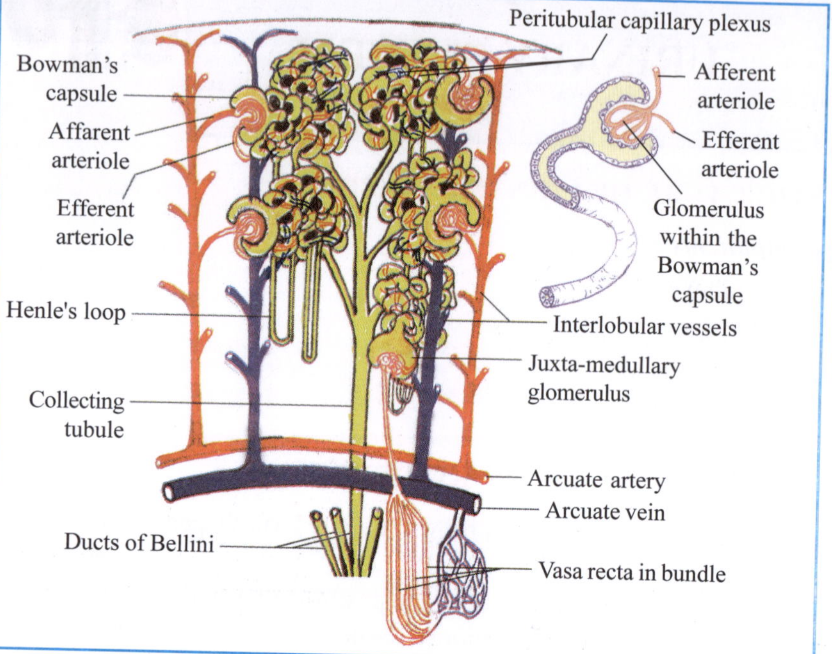

Fig. 7.2 Renal tubules and vessels (Diagramatic).

The apex of a pyramid projects into a small funnel shaped structure known as **calyx minor**. One calyx minor receives 1 to 3 papillae. Several calyces minors unite to form **major calyces** which are generally two or sometimes three in number. These major calyces join together to form the **pelvis** of the kidney. From the pelvis ureter begins. At the medial border of the kidney there is a depression known as **renal sinus** which accommodates the renal pelvis, renal artery, renal vein, nerves and lymphatics. Spaces in between the structures remain filled with fat.

Structure

Capsule

The whole of the organ remains covered by a capsule which is composed of collagen, elastic and smooth muscle fibers. The capsule is surrounded by perirenal fat which is continuous with the fat of renal sinus.

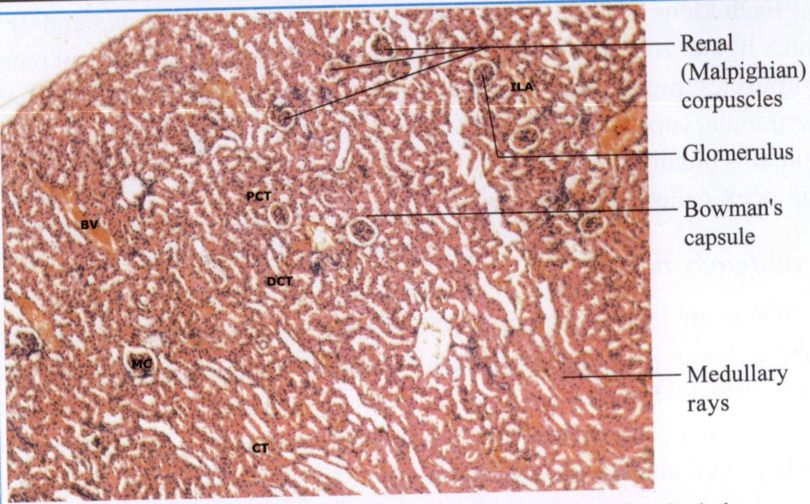

PCT – Proximal convoluted tubule ; DCT – Distal convoluted tubule ;
CT – Collecting tubules ; BV – Blood vessel

Fig. 7.3 Kidney (cortex).

1. Renal (Malpighian) corpuscles consisting of Bowman's capsule and glomerulus are numerous ;
2. Proximal and distal convoluted tubules are plenty ;
3. Collecting tubules are observed within medullary rays.

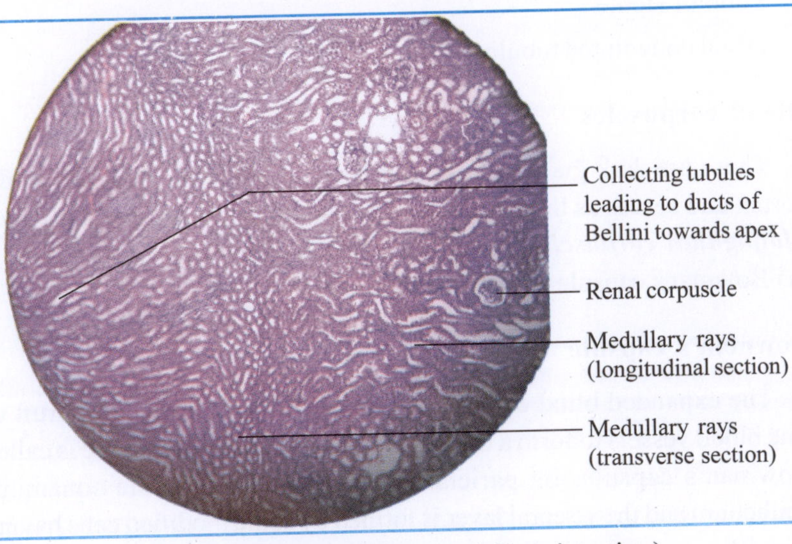

Fig. 7.4 Kidney (cortico-medullary junction).

Each kidney exhibits 1) a peripheral dark part – the cortex and 2) a inner lighter zone – the medulla. The cortex is composed mainly of renal corpuscles, proximal convoluted tubules, distal convoluted tubules and peritubular capillary plexus and that is why darker is colour. The medulla contains bundles of straight collecting tubules which converge towards the apex called ***medullary rays***.

Uriniferous tubules

These are the main components of a kidney. Each of the uriniferous tubule is composed of two parts – a) Nephron and b) collecting tubule. These tubules are responsible for excretion and collection of urine. The whole length of a uriniferous tubule is lined by a single layer of epithelial cells placed on a basement membrane.

Nephron

It is the structural and functional unit of the kidney and comprises of a convoluted tubular system with a blind distal end which is invested by capillaries. Each nephron has following parts :

Renal corpuscle

Proximal convoluted tubule

Loop of Henle

Distal convoluted tubule

Renal corpuscles

These are dark granules (about 0.2 mm in diameter) situated in the cortex and serves as the main filtration apparatus. These are also called ***Malpighian corpuscles***. Each corpuscle is composed of two parts – (a) Bowmans capsule and (b) Glomerulus.

Bowman's capsule

The expanded blind end of the nephron is invaginated by a truft of fine blood vessels to form a double layered cup shaped structure is called Bowman's capsule. Its parietal layer is lined by simple squamous epithelium and the visceral layer is formed by some modified cells having feet like processes called **podocytes**. Between the foot processes

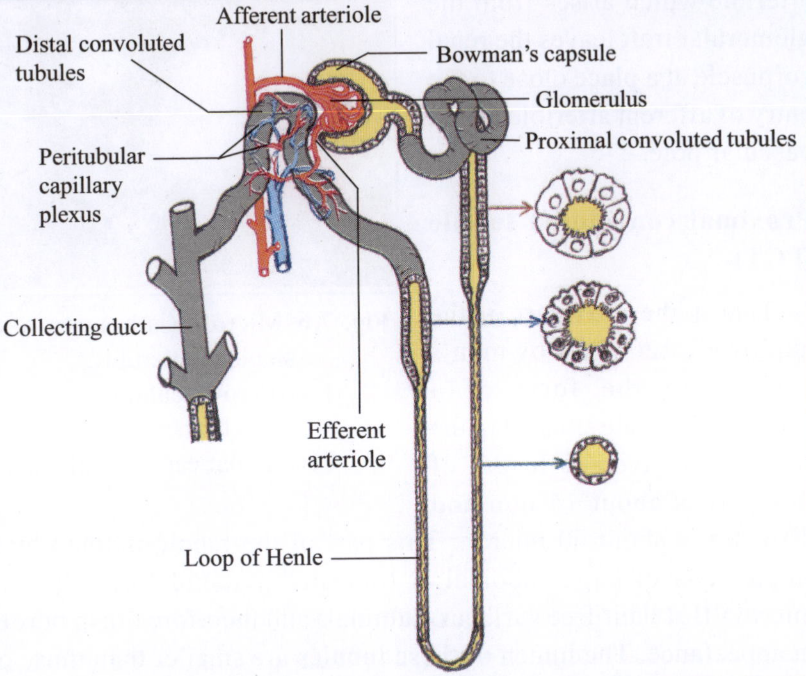

Fig. 7.5 Structure of a nephron (Diagramatic).

(pedicles) there are tiny spaces called filtration sites. The dialyzing membrane between the blood and glomerular filtrate is formed by the basal lamina of podocytes and endothelial lining of glomerular capillaries. Around the capillaries some phagocytic cells are found called **mesangial** cells. The space between the parietal and visceral layers of Bowman's capsule which is continuous with proximal convoluted tubule is known as capsular space.

Glomerulus

The afferent arteriole a branch of interlobular artery while invaginating the Bowman's capsule breaks down into numerous capillaries which club together to form a lobulated tuft called glomerulus. The lining endothelial cells of these capillaries are perforated by numerous pores of about 0.1 micron diameter. About 30 to 40 capillaries arise from an afferent arteriole to form a glomerular tuft which again re-unite to form efferent arteriole. The efferent arteriole which arises from the glomerular traft leaves the renal corpuscle at a place close to the entry of afferent arteriole called vascular pole.

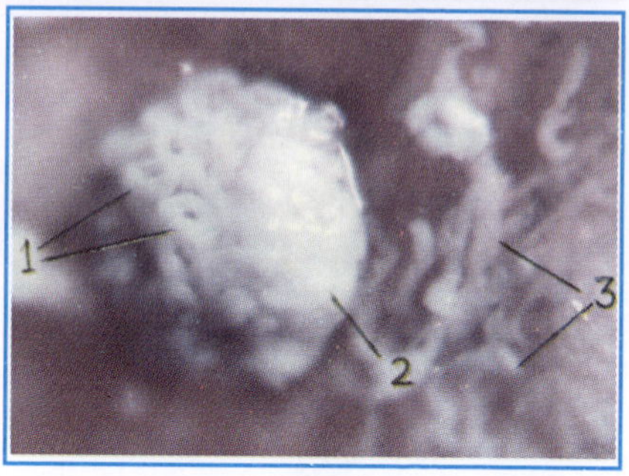

Fig. 7.6 Microfil (latex) cast of a single glomerulus.
1 – Microvascular loops,
2 – Glomerulus,
3 – Peritubular capillary plexus.

Proximal convoluted tubule (PCT)

This is the next part of the nephron after the Bowman's capsule in the form of a convoluted tubule situated in the cortex. The average length of this part is about 14 mm and diameter is about 60 micron. This part of the tubule is lined by a single layer of large cuboidal or truncated pyramidal cells having microvilli at their free surfaces (luminal) and therefore brush border in appearance. The lumen of these tubules are smaller than those of distal convoluted tubules. The basal portion of these cells show infoldings.

The main function of proximal convoluted tubule is to re-absorbe about 80% of the filtrate which contains water, electrolytes, glucose, amino acids and small proteins. The microvilli and interdigitations are probably responsible for such functions. The terminal part of PCT becomes straight and continuous with the descending limb of Loop of Henle.

Loop of Henle

This is an U shaped loop formed between the proximal and distal convoluted tubules and has a descending limb and an ascending limb. These loops are mostly located in the medulla and partly in the cortex.

Descending limb is continuous with the PCT. Its upper part is lined by simple cuboidal epithelium and lower part by simple squamous epithelium.

Ascending limb is continuous with the thin segment of desceding limb after the loop and lined by the same simple squamous epithelium at the lower part and simple caboid epithelium at its upper part.

The loops of cortical nephrons which constitute 80-85% of the total number, are short but those situated at the deep layer near the medulla (juxta medullary nephrons) have long loops and located in the medulla.

Distal convoluted Tubules (DCT)

The ascending limb is continuous with the next part of the nephron which is convoluted again between the afferent and effecent arterioles of the glomerulus. It is located in the cortex of the kidney. The lumen is larger than that of PCT. A single layer of small cuboidal cells line the DCT. Instead of brush border, a few micro villi are present on the free surface of these epithelial cells. Infoldings are also seen at the basal plasma of this part of tubule. With the influence of Aldesterone (from posterior pituitary) permeability of DCT to water is increased.

The terminal part of the DCT joins with the collecting tubules. However a small junctional or connecting tubule connects the nephron with the straight collecting tubule which are situated at the medullary rays of the cortex. The collecting tubules while entering the medullary ray join with similar tubules several times.

The junctional tubule and collecting tubules are lined by cuboidal to columnar cells having clear cytoplasm. Microvilli are absent.

Types of nephrons – They are two types.

a) ***Cortical nephrons*** – They are numerous (about 85% of total)

Efferent arterioles are narrower than afferent.

Loop of Henle is shorter, ascending limb is thicker and extends upto the basal zone of pyramid.

Situated mostly in the cortex.

b) ***Juxta-medullary nephrons*** – They are less in number (15% of total)

Efferent and afferent arterioles are of similar thickness.

Henle's loop is long and extends close to the apical zone of pyramid.

Ascending limb is thin at the beginning and then becomes thick.

Situated adjacent to medulla.

Juxta-glomerular apparatus (JGA)

This is a complex formed by the part of Distal convoluted tubule, Afferent arteriole and some extraglomerular mesangial cells. The main components are – Macula densa, Juxtaglomerular cells and Lacis cells.

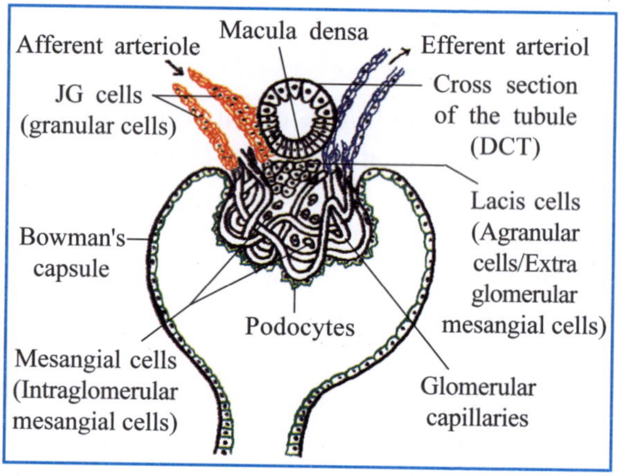

Fig. 7.7 Juxtaglomerular apparatus.
(By Courtesy : Dr. A.B.S. Mahapatra)

Macula densa is a row of tightly packed cells lining the part of DCT which is in contact of afferent and efferent arterioles.

Juxta-glomerular cells are modified smooth muscle cells of the tunica media of afferent arteriole. These cells have granules which contain rennin and act as barorecepter.

Lacis cells (Polkissen cells) – These are agranular mesangial cells found in the triangular space formed by afferent arteriole, efferent arteriole and macula densa and therefore extra glomerular in position. These cells probably transmit sensory signal to JG cells.

The JGA by its tubuloglomerular feedback mechanism regulates flow of blood through glomerular vessels and thereby controls glomerular filtration rate. The macula densa helps secretion of rennin from the JG cells. Renin helps in the local production of Angiotensin II which constricts efferent arteriole and thereby control flow of blood through glomerular capillaries and in turn regulates filtration.

Collecting tubules – The collecting tubules, as has been mentioned earlier proceed towards the medulla collectively after joining with similar adjacent tubes several times and form the medullary ray. Finally such 20-25 tubules open at the apex of the pyramid (renal papilla) as the ***ducts of Bellini***.

Renal Papillae

These are the apexes of renal pyramid which project into minor calyces in the renal sinus. The papillae are composed the terminal parts of the collecting tubules, loops of Henle of juxtamedullary glomeruli and Vasa recta. The renal papilla is covered by transitional epithelium which also enter for a short distance into the papillary ducts (ducts of Bellini). The papillary ducts empty into minor calyces.

The calyces minor as well as calyces major are lined by transitional epithelium having 2 to 3 layers of cells.

Blood vessels of the kidney

Since the function of this organ is directly related to blood vessels, a brief description of their distribution is important.

Just a little before or at the point of entry into the kidney the renal artery divides into few segmental arteries. Each of them again divides into few inter-lobar arteries in the sinus. Each inter-lobar artery passes between renal pyramids and at the cortico-medullary junction breaks up into arch shaped arcuate arteries without anastomosing with adjacent arcuate arterier. From arcuate arteries numerous parallel arteries arise almost in right angles and proceed towards cortex. These are interlobular arteries. These vessels give off a number of side branches called afferent arterioles which form glomerular tufts in the Bowman's capsule and finally form efferent arterioles. In case of cortical glomeruli the efferent arterioles are of less in caliber and divide to form peritubular capillary plexus around PCT, DCT and loops of Henle and join the interlobular vein. Juxta medullary glomeruli receive afferent arterioles from the beginning of the interlobular arteries. The efferent arterioles of these glomeruli are of same caliber to those of afferent which break into numerous parallel vessels and proceed towards the medulla between the loops of Henle and collecting tubules. These bundles of parallel vessels are called ***vasa recta***. They form hairpin loops, renturn to the cortico-medullary junction, re-unite to form venule and enter the arcuate vein directly. The loops of Henle act as the counter current multipliers and vasa recta work as counter current exchanger in the process of medullary concentration gradient.

Ureter

These are a pair of slender long tubes extend from the corresponding kidney to the bladder. Each ureter begins within the renal sinus as a funnel shaped dilatation, the pelvis of the ureter, formed by the union of major calyces and passes downward medially through the hilum and continue with the abdominal part. The wall is composed of a) Outer fibrous layer, b) Middle muscular layer and c) Inner mucous layer.

a) The outer fibrous layer consists of Collagen and reticular fibers.

b) The middle muscular layer is made up of an inner longitudinal and outer circular layer at the upper two third part. In lower one third part there is an additional outer longitudinal layer. Intervening connective tissue is present between these layers.

c) The inner mucous layer is formed by transitional epithelium which consists of 4 to 5 layers of cells. The lumen appears to be star shaped in transverse section due to foldings of the mucous membrane in non distended condition.

Urinary bladder

This oval elongated sac is the store house of urine. The composition of the wall is similar to that of ureter but is more thick at the neck due to its muscular layer. The outer fibrous layer is covered by a serous coat at its upper end. The fibrous layer attaches the bladder with surrounding organs. The muscular layer is thick and consists of an inner longitudinal middle circular and outer longitudinal layer. However, in some places these bundles are mixed up due to interlacing between muscular bundles of different layers. The outer longitudinal muscle layer is continuous with the muscle of prostate. The in between connective tissue contains numerous ganglia. Circular layer is more thick at the neek to form internal

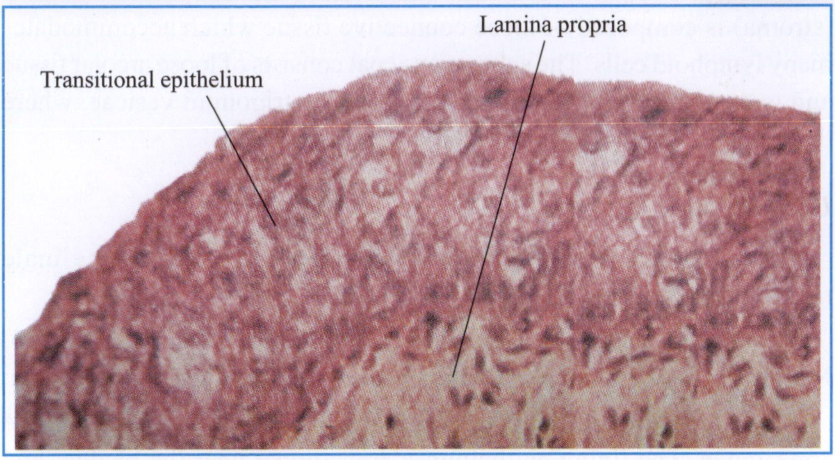

Fig. 7.8 Transitional epithelium lining the urinary bladder.

1. Mucous membrane is lined by transitional epithelium with 6-8 laters of cells ;
2. Lamina propria is loose in appearance ;
3. Muscularis mucosae is absent.

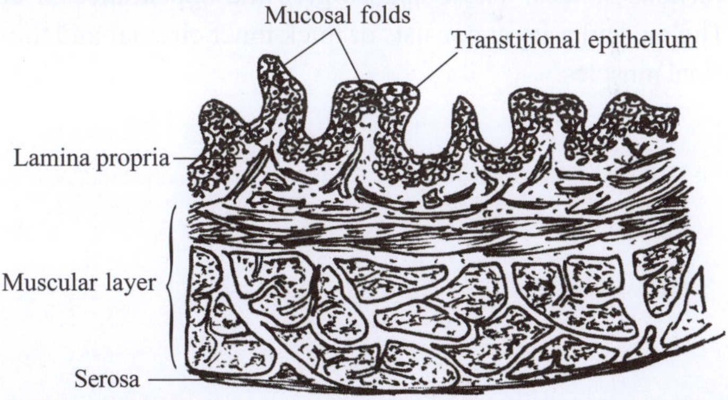

Fig. 7.9 Section of the wall of urinary bladder (diagramatic).

sphincter of the internal urethral orifice. Such muscle sphincter at the neck of the bladder is not present in females. However spirally arranged muscles in the wall of female urethra may serve the purpose of sphincter vesicae. The mucous layer is thrown into many folds and composed of transtitional epithelium with 6 to 8 layers of cells. This is also popularly called urothelium. Mucous glands are almost absent. Lamina propria (stroma) is composed of loose connective tissue which accommodates many lymphoid cells. The submucous coat consists of loose areolar tissue and is present all over the bladder except the trigonum vesicae, where the mucous membrane is adherent to the muscle.

Urethra (female)

The structure of male urethra has been discussed in the male reproductive system.

The female urethra is composed of a) an outer adventitial layer, b) Middle muscular layer, c) Sub mucous layer and d) Inner mucous layer.

The mucosa is folded and therefore the lumen presents stellate appearance. The lining epithelium is transitional near the bladder and gradually changes to stratified squamous epithelium at the external urethral orifice. In between them a small part lined by psendostratified cuboidal or columnar epithelium.

The sub-mucous layer is compact at the adjacent area of the epithelium. It is composed of fibro elastic tissue, diffuse lymphatic tissue and cavernous spaces. These spaces give the appearance of erectile tissue. The muscular layer consists of thick inner circular and thin outer longitudinal muscles.

8
REPRODUCTIVE SYSTEM

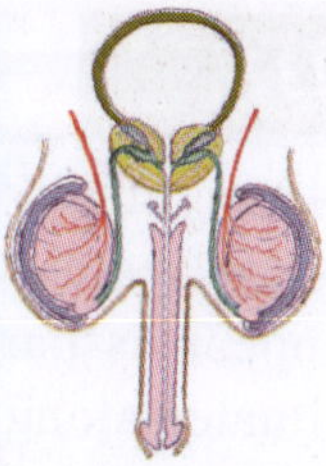

MALE REPRODUCTIVE SYSTEM

Components :

1. **Testis** – one pair
2. **Ducts** – a) Vasa efferentia
   b) Duct of Epididymis
   c) Vas deferens
   d) Ejaculatory duct
3. **Penis**
4. **Glands** – a) Seminal vesicles
   b) Prostate
   c) Bulbo urethral gland

TESTIS

This ovoid male sex gland is placed within the scrotal sac and responsible for production of male germ cells i.e. Spermatozoa and male sex hormone i.e. testosterone.

The whole of the gland is covered by tunica albugenia, a thick fibrous capsule. Outside tunica albugenia the gland is covered by tunica vaginalis propria, which is derived from processus vaginalis of peritoneum. The parital layer of tunica vaginalis *i.e.* tunica vaginalis reflexa remains attached to the inner wall of scrotum.

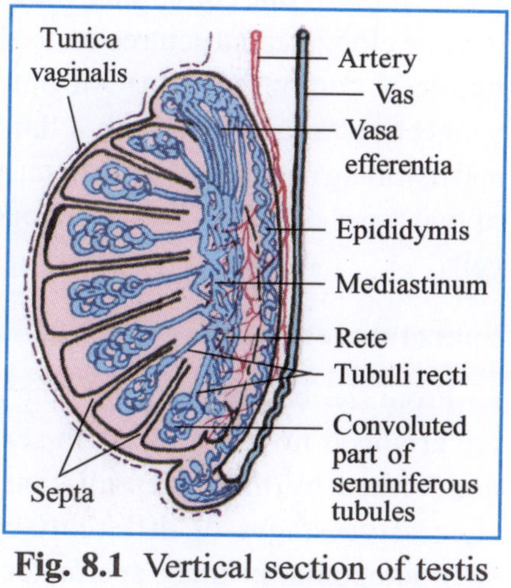

Fig. 8.1 Vertical section of testis (diagramatic).

The outer layer of testis, ***tunica albugenia*** is thick and composed of collagen and elastic fibers. The deep layer of tunica albugenia contains numerous blood vessels and hence termed ***tunica vasculosa***. Numerous septa appear as partition walls radiating from the ***mediastinum testis*** situated along the posterior border of the gland and divide the testis into about 250 compartments known as lobules of testis. The trabeculae or septa are composed of collagen fibers, vessels and nerves. The connective tissue elements of the septa are continuous with the intralobular connective tissue. Each of the lobules accommodates several highly convoluted ***seminiferous tubules*** and interstitial tissue between them. The convoluted tubules become straight at the apex of the lobule and enter the ***mediastinum testis***. Here the tubules coming from adjacent lobules join each other and form a network, the ***rete testis***. The convoluted part is called ***tubuli contorti***, straight part directed towards mediastinum known as ***tubuli recti*** and the network portion within mediastinum is called ***rete testis***. The upper end of rete testis is connected to a number (10–15) small ductules called ***vasa efferentia*** which come out of the proximal end of testis and enter into the head of epididymis. These tubules are lined by pseudo-stratified columnar epithelium. They unite together to form the single duct of epididymis.

Seminiferous tubules

Sectoins of this convoluted tubules appear as a collecton of round or oval or elongated structures under light microscope. The wall of each tubule is composed of a) An outer capsule consists of fibroelastic connective tissue along with a thin homogenous basement membrane and b) Lining of cuboidal epithelium arranged in several layers and consists of two types of cells – i) Spermatogenic cells and ii) Supporting Sertoli cells.

Spermatogenic cells

From the basement membrane and towards the lumen, these cells are arranged in 4 to 8 layers in sexually matured persons. These cells are formed by the differentiation of the basal cuboidal cells. Four successive stages of differentiation can be recognized. These are spermatogonia, primary spermatocytes, secondary spermatocytes and spermatids.

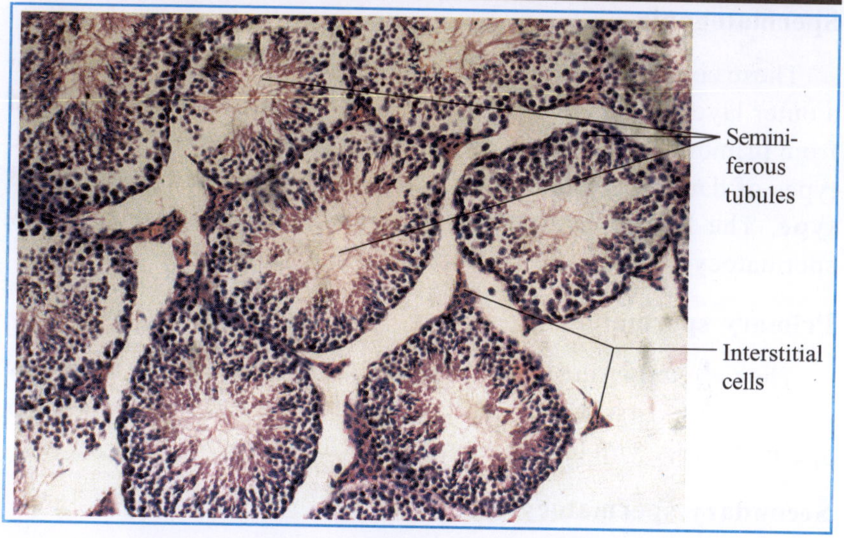

Fig. 8.2 Section of testis (low magnification).

1. Sections of seminiferous tubules are mostly oval in shape ;
2. Interstitial cells of Leydig are present in between the tubules ;
3. Within the seminiferous tubules the spermatogenic cells are arranged in layers ;
4. Few Sertoli cells are also detected in higher magnification.

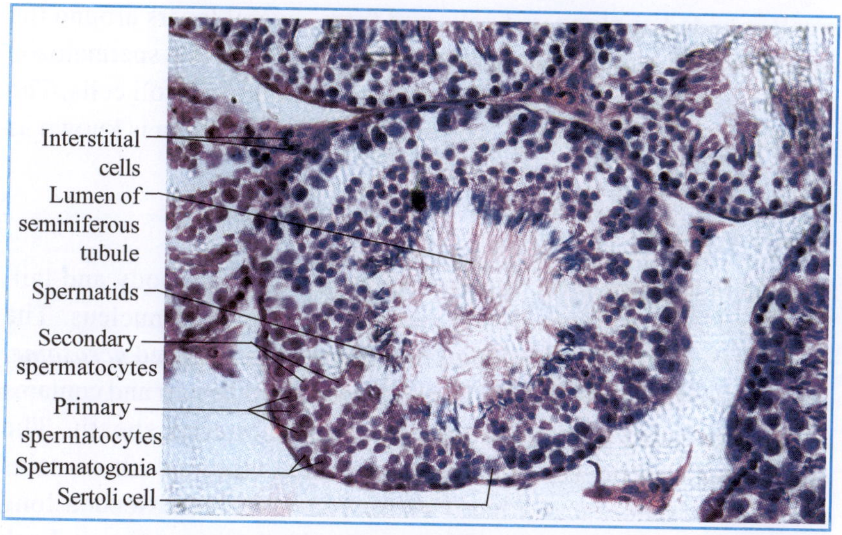

Fig. 8.3 Section of testis (higher magnification).

Spermatogonia

These cells rest on a basal lamina between Sertoli cells and form a outer layer of cuboidal cells with small nuclei. These are derived from primordial germ cells. They divide mitotically and form three types of daughter cells – a) **Pale A type**, b) **Dark A type** and c) **B type**. The B type spermatogonia differentiate to form primary spermatocytes.

Primary spermatocytes

They are larger in size and contain large spherical nuclei. These cells undergo first meotic (reduction) division and form secondary spermatocytes with haploid number of chromosomes.

Secondary spermatocytes

These are smaller in size with small nuclei and half number (23,X or 23,Y) of chromosomes. Generally half of these cells contain X type and other half of cells contain Y type sex chromosomes.

Spermatids

Each secondary spermatocyte undergoes second meotic (non-reduction) division and gives rise to spermatids. The spermatids are small rounded or elongated cells and form several layers around the lumen of the tubule. The spermatids are transformed into spermatozoa and for some time remain attached to the apexes of Sertoli cells. The process of transformation of spermatid to spermatozoon is known as spermiogenesis.

Spermatozoon

This is a motile structure and composed of head, body and tail. The head is oval in shape and contains a condensed nucleus. The anterior two-third is covered by a bilamilar head cap called ***acrosome***. It is derived from Golgi body. The body is the middle part and contains axial fillaments surrounded by the mitochondrial sheath. The constricted part between the head and body is the neck. It contains proximal centriole and a basal body. The tail is an extended long structure accommodates axial fillaments and helps in movement. Each spermatozoon contain either X (female) or Y (male) sex-chromosome. The head is about 3-4μ thick and the total length of a spermatozoon is about 60-65μ.

Sertoli cells

These are elongated fairly large cells situated between the spermatogenic cells. The bases of these cells are attached to the basement membrane and contain large vesicular oval nucleus. The free ends are extended towards the lumen and give attachment to many developing spermatozoa. Sertoli cells provide mechanical support and nutrition to the developing spermatozoa.

Interstitial tissue

Clusters of cells situated in between the seminiferous tubules are called interstitial cells or cells of Leydig. These cells contain large spherical nuclei, acidophilic cytoplasm and remain surrounded by loose vascular connective tissue. This is the endocrine part of testis and secrets testosterone and small amount of estrogen.

DUCTS

Efferent ductules

These ductules (10-20) arise from the upper end of rete testis and enter into the head of epididymis. Although the tubules of rete testis are lined by flattened epithelium, the efferent ductules are lined by ciliated columnar epithelium and are surrounded by circularly disposed smooth muscle fibers.

Duct of Epididymis

The wall of this duct comprises of a) an outer coat and b) lining epithelium. The lumen is large and contains bunches of spermatozoa. The outer wall is composed of smooth muscle and elastic fibers. The lumen is lined by pseudostratified columnar epithelium containing mainly tall columnar cells and some small basal cells. The free surface of these tall cells possess stereocillia. This highly convoluted tube provides accommodation and nutrition to the spermatozoa.

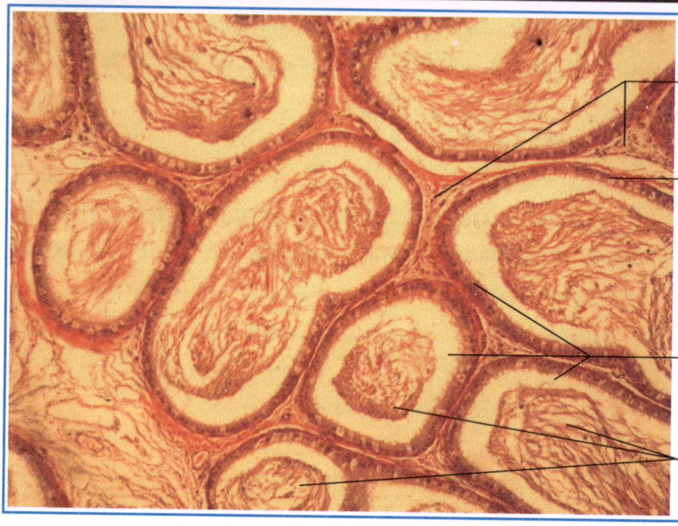

Fig. 8.4 Section of epididymis.

1. The lumen of the duct of epididymis contains large mass of spermatozoa ;
2. The duct is lined by pseudostratified columnar epithelium ;
3. The epithelial cells bear non motile cilia (stereocilia).

Vas Deferens

This long tube extends from the tail of epididymis, becomes incorporated in the spermatic cord, traverses the inguinal canal, reaches the base of the bladder and forms a dilatation, the ampulla. It joins with the duct of seminal vesicle at the base of the prostate to form ***ejaculatory duct***. This common duct opens in the prostatic urethra at the colliculus seminalis along with the similar duct of other side. The wall of this tube is thick and the lumen is narrow. It is composed of an outer fibrous coat, middle muscular coat and an inner

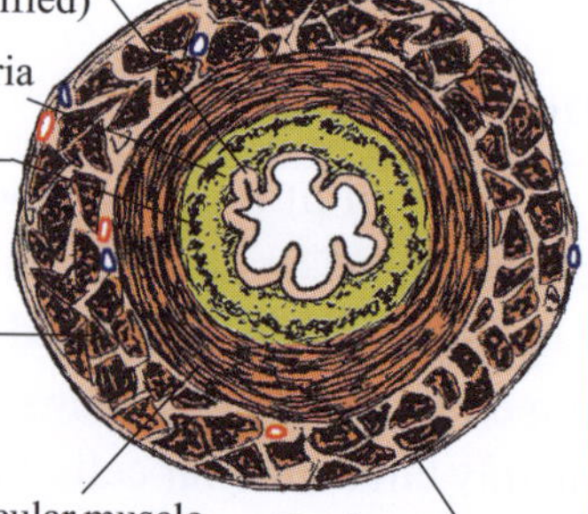

Fig. 8.5 Vas deferens.

mucous coat. A) Outer fibrous coat – It is composed of fibroelastic tissue containing numerous blood vessels, nerves and scattered bundles of smooth muscle fibers. B) Middle muscular coat – This is very thick and composed of outer longitudinal, middle circular and inner longitudinal muscle fibers. C) Inner mucous coat – Some longitudinal folds are present in this layer. It is lined by pseudo-stratified epithelium comprises mainly of columnar cells and few basal cells. Some of these cells contain stereocilia. The lumen of the ampulla portion is large and has more longitudinal folds. Submucosa is highly vascularised and composed of loose connective tissue.

Urethra (male)

The whole of the urethral mucosa is thrown into longitudinal folds which disappear during time of erection and micturation. The prostatic part (bladder to caudal edge of prostate) is generally lined by transitional epithelium. A slightly raised dorsomedian fold of the mucosa of this part form the **colliculus seminalis**. The said lining of the other two portions – membranous part (from the level of prostate gland to the ischial arch) and penile part is made up of stratified columnar or cuboidal epithelium. Within the penis the mucosa presents some depressions where urethral glands open into the urethra. Terminal fossa and external urethral orifice is lined by non keratinised stratified squamous epithelium. The lamina submucosa of urethra is composed of dense irregular connective tissue, smooth muscle fibers and diffuse lymphatic tissue. The tunica muscularis of prostatic part is composed of mainly longitudinal smooth muscle fibers.

PENIS

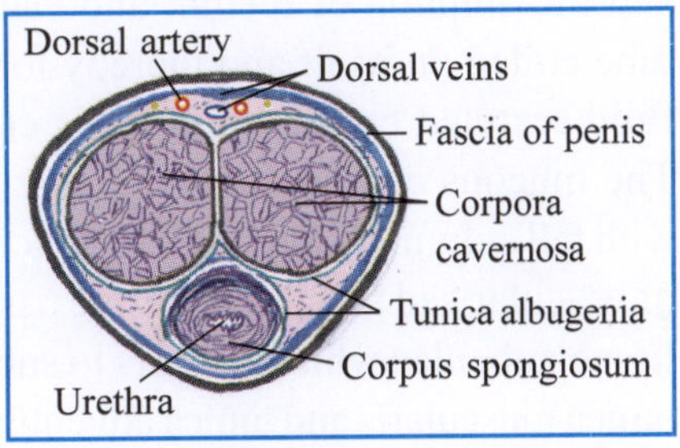

Fig. 8.6 Transverse section of the body of penis.

The penis consists of two parts – a body and a root. The body is composed of three fibro-elastic cylinders. These are – a pair of corpora cavernosa, situated at the dorsal aspect and one corpus spongisum, situated at the ventral aspect of this rod shaped copulatory organ. The tunica albugenia surrounds the corpora cavernosa and send tabeculae or septa inside. These septa are composed of fibraelastic and smooth muscle fibers and form boundaries of cavernous space for erectile tissue. The septal arteries give rise to capillaries which open into cavernous spaces. The corpus spongiosum possesses similar structures to that of corpora cavernosa but the septa are of finer variety and cavernous spaces are less in number.

The root is composed of the diverging crura and a median bulb of the penis. In the body the two crura continue as corpora cavernosa along the dorsal aspect and the bulb continues as corpus spongiosum at the ventral aspect. The urethra passes through the entire length of corpus spongiosum which situated along the ventral longitudinal groove formed by the two cylinders of corpora cavernosa. Corpora cavernosa and corpus spongiosum are separately enveloped by tunica albugenia.

Outside the tunica albugenia the penis is enclosed by ***superficial fascia*** and ***skin*** from inside outwards. The outer layer of superficial fascia is made up of loose areolar tissue and the inner one which is well defined, called *fascia of penis*. The fascia accommodates dorsal vein of penis at the middle, a pair of dorsal arteries of penis on each side of the vein and a pair of dorsal nerves lateral to the arteries. The skin covering the penis is loose and generally dark in colour. It is reflected over the glans as a fold of prepuce at the neck of the penis.

GLANDS

Seminal Vesicle

These are a pair of glands situated between the base of the bladder and the ampulla of rectum and each of them is composed of a single tube coiled on itself and thereby lobulated in appearance. The seminal fluid secreted by the lining cells contribute a large part of the semen. The mucous coat is made up of pseudostratified columnar epithelium with tall columnar and small spherical cells. The submucosa is composed of vascularised loose connective tissue. It is continuous with connective tissue trabeulae which appears to subdivide the organ into lobules. A thin tunica muscularis and tunica adventitia surrounds the organ. The secretary epithelium is folded. The duct of seminal vesicle join with the terminal part of vas and form the ejaculatory duct.

Prostate

This structure surrounds the prostatic urethra and composed of numerous tubuloalveolar glands embedded in the framework of fibromuscular tissue. Two portions of the gland is recognized – an external part is called ***corpus prostatae*** and an internal portion called ***pars disseminata***. The gland is encapsulated with a layer of collagen, elastic and smooth muscle fibers. In the external portion the glands and their ducts are surrounded by fibromuscular connective tissue. Trabeculae which are mostly muscular in the external part originate from the capsule. Numerous septa divide the organ into 30-50 separate compound tubulo-alveolar glands. Each gland has it's own duct which opens into the prostatic urethra. The tubules and alveoli are lined by simple cuboidal or columnar epithelium and sometimes by pseudo stratified columnar epithelium depending on its phase of activity. These branched tubules have dilated ends and in section they appears as follicles of different shapes and sizes. The ducts are sometimes lined by two layers of cells. The secretion is thin milky, slightly alkaline and form a considerable part of seminal fluid. It contains acid phosphatase, fibrinolysin, prostaglandin and prostate specific antigen (PSA). Elevated level of PSA in circulation

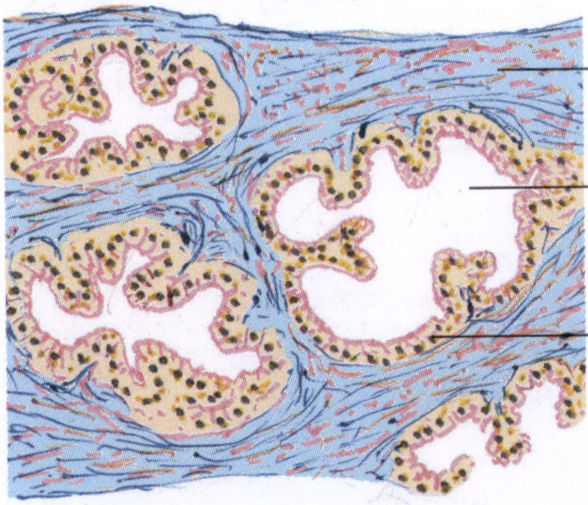

Fig. 8.7 Section of the prostate gland (reconstituted).

1. Tubulo-alveolar pattern of the glands is clear ;
2. The glands are embedded in the framework of fibromuscular tissue ;
3. Columnar variety of cells are seen in the epithelium.

is the indication for abnormal glandular mucosa typically due to prostatic carcinoma or inflammation.

In old men, some calcified mass which are formed by concretion of secretions are found in the lumen of the gland. These are called *Corpora amylacea*.

Bulbourethral gland (Gland of Cowper)

These are two small rounded structures (1 cm diameter), lie above the bulb of penis. It is composed of several lobules. Each lobule is made up of a number of acini which are lined by columnar epithelium. A single duct from each gland, about 3 cm long, opens on the floor of spongiose part of urethra.

FEMALE REPRODUCTIVE SYSTEM

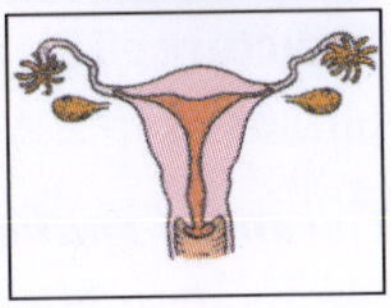

Components :

a) Ovaries – two
b) Uterine tubes – two
c) Uterus – one
d) Vagina
e) Vulva

Accessory sex gland – Mammary glands

OVARIES

These are two oval bodies, one on each side, situated adjacent to lateral pelvic wall and are attached to the posterior layer of broad ligament by a fold of peritoneum known as masovarium. Each ovary is placed close to the fimbriated end of the fallopian tube so that it remains adjacent to pelvic osteum. It is dull grey in colour and the size is like an almond. The surface is irregular in a mature ovary which is smooth before puberty.

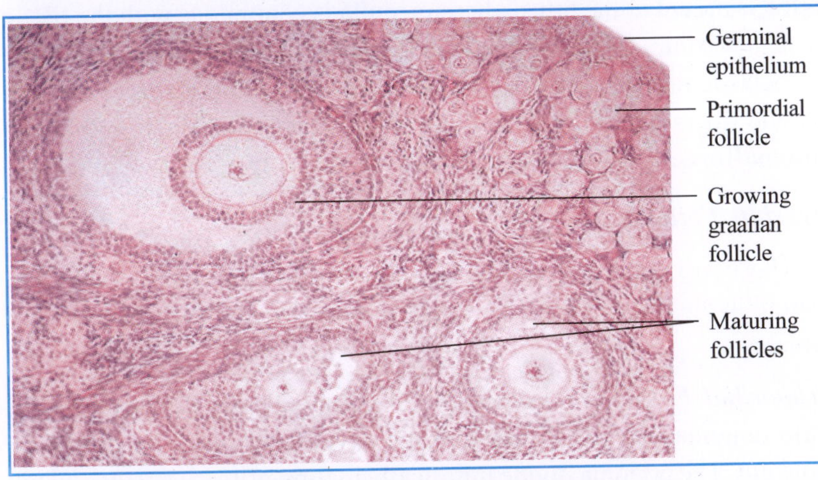

Fig. 8.8 Section of an ovary.

1. Ovarian follicles in different stages of development are observed ;
2. Germinal epithelium is thin ;
3. Stroma is rich in blood vessels ;
4. Graafian follicle and few maturing follicles are seen.

Structure : This organ exhibits maximum histological variations in various phases of life. A normal mature ovary has the following structures.

Germinal epithelium : It is the external covering of the ovary formed by a single layer of cuboidal cells on a basement membrane. This is actually a modified peritoneum. It is misnomer because none of the follicles develop from this layer.

Tunica albugenia : This is a thin capsule of collagen fibers encloses the ovary and situated deep to the germinal epithelium.

Ovarian Stroma : It consists of reticular fibers and spindle shaped stromal cells (connective tissue) looks like smooth muscle but have no fibrils in their cytoplasm and are not contractile. The interstitial cells are derived from stromal cells. The ovarian tissue is composed of an outer cortex and an inner medulla. The ***cortex*** is the outer thicker part situated between tunica albugenia and medulla. It is dense, less vascular and contains a) Stromal cells, b) Ovarian follicles in different stages of development and regression and c) Corpus luteum. However, the cortical tissue is absent at the hilus where medulla is continuous with the tissue of mesovarium. ***Medulla*** is placed centrally and composed of loose fibroelastic tissue, plenty of tortuous as well as some scattered smooth muscle fibers, blood vessels, lymphatics, nerves and small number of chromaffin cells.

Ovarian Follicles

These are spherical vesicle like structures which are formed and mature in the ovary during the fertile period (puberty to menopause) of females.

Primordial Follicle : The primordial germ cells are differentiated to form oogonia when they reach to the developing ovary by migrating from gut. The oogonia divide mitotically to form primary oocytes which become surrounded by a single layer of epithelial cells, known as **primordial follicle**. These epithelial cells are flat in shape and are derived from the epithelium which covers the ovary. The epithelial covering may be complete or incomplete. The number of primordial follicles is few lakhs in new born out of which near about 40,000 follicles persist at puberty. Degeneration of primordial follicles mostly occurs in the early part of life. After puberty 5-12 follicles undergo the process of maturation in each menstrual cycle out of which one follicle from any of the two ovaries becomes fully matures.

Primary Follicle : The surrounding flatten cells become cuboidal and proliferate by mitosis to form multilayerd mass of the follicle. The ***zona pellucida***, a homogenous transparent membrane is formed around the primary oocyte. At this stage the follicle is called **Primary follicle** which has a diameter of about 120-140 microns.

Secondary Follicle : At the peripheral layer the follicular cells become enveloped by a layer called theca folliculi. Its outer dense fibrous and flat cellular layer is called ***theca externa*** and the inner cellular and vascular layer is called ***theca interna***. A number of fluid filled spaces appear between the follicular cells which coalesce to form a single cavity called antrum. The oocyte is pushed eccentrically. The antrum accommodates a fluid called liquor folliculi.

Graafian Follicle : The secondary follicle undergoes further maturation along with the ovum in it. The diameter of the follicle may be 10-15 mm and that of ovum becomes 100-150 microns. The antrum increases with the enhancement of liquor folliculi and thereby the follicular cells are divided into a peripheral part kown as ***membrana granulosa*** and an inner layer surrounding ovum called ***cumulus oophorus***. Adjacent to the zona pellucida some cells of the cumulus oophorus are arranged in a radiating manner and called ***corona radiata***. The oocyte becomes more eccentric and in one area the membrana granulosa and cumulus oophorus cells are in contact with each other. This area along with the cells is called ***discus proligerus***. At this stage first meotic reduction division takes place with the formation of a large Secondary oocyte and the first polar body. Both the structures remain within the zona pellucida

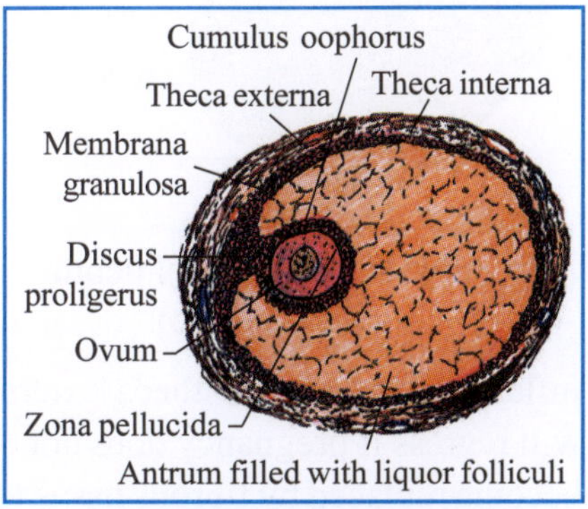

Fig. 8.9 Graafian follicle (diagramatic).

and contain half number of Chromosomes. The cell membrane of this Secondary oocytes is now called **Vitelline membrane**.

Ovulation

Rupture of mature Graafian follicle and release of ovum in the peritoneal cavity is known as ovulation. The ovum surrounded by cumulus oophorus comes out of the follicle as well as of the ovary at the time of ovulation. Generally ovum is released at a time from alternate or any one of the ovaries, is swallowed by the funnel shaped fimbriated end of the fallopian tube.

Corpus Luteum (C.L.) : After ovulation, the follicular cells re-organize to form a structure along with some amount of blood known as ***Corpora hemorrhagicum***, which in turn develops into a yellow coloured endocrine gland – the corpus luteum. The membrana granulosa and theca interna becomes folded and theca externa sends connective tissue inwards. The granulosa cells are arranged as a thick in-folded stratified layer around the left-over central cavity. These cells with abundant cytoplasm containing lipid droplets and yellowish pigments are called ***granulosa-lutin cells***. These cells secrete Progesterone. The cells of theca interna are converted to ***theca-lutin cells*** and secrete Estrogen. This development occurs due to the influence of LH. The theca externa encapsulate the gland. The C.L. will regress if pregnancy does not occur. The lutin cells degenerate and become replaced by fibrous tissue to form corpus albicans. If pregnancy occurs, the C.L. becomes enlarged and continues secretion of progesterone during the first half of the pregnancy. It starts degenerating after wards with the production of progesterone by placenta and finally replaced by corpus albicans.

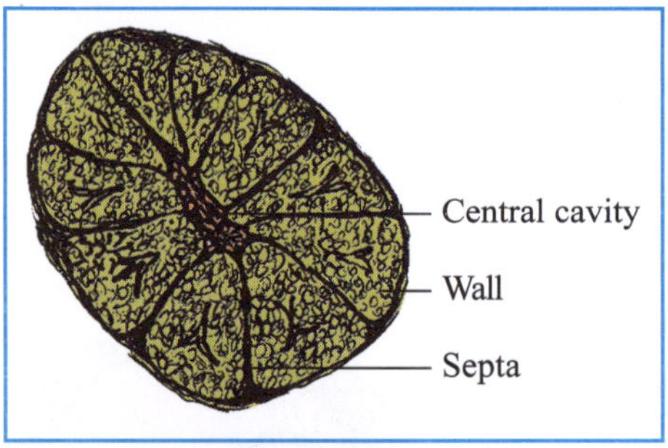

Fig. 8.10 Corpus luteum (diagramatic).

Atretic Follicles : Many of the primordial follicles or growing follicles degenerate and disappear without being matured. This process is known as atresia. At first the ovum degenerates and then the follicular cells follow. The space become replaced by stroma. Atresia mostly occurs in the early part of life and before puberty. Some cells of theca interna of atretic follicles form groups of epitheloid cells in the ovarian stroma, called Interstitial cells which secrete estrogen.

FALLOPIAN TUBE

All the different parts of the tube – Infundibulum, Ampula, Isthmus and Intramural have a common histological structure.

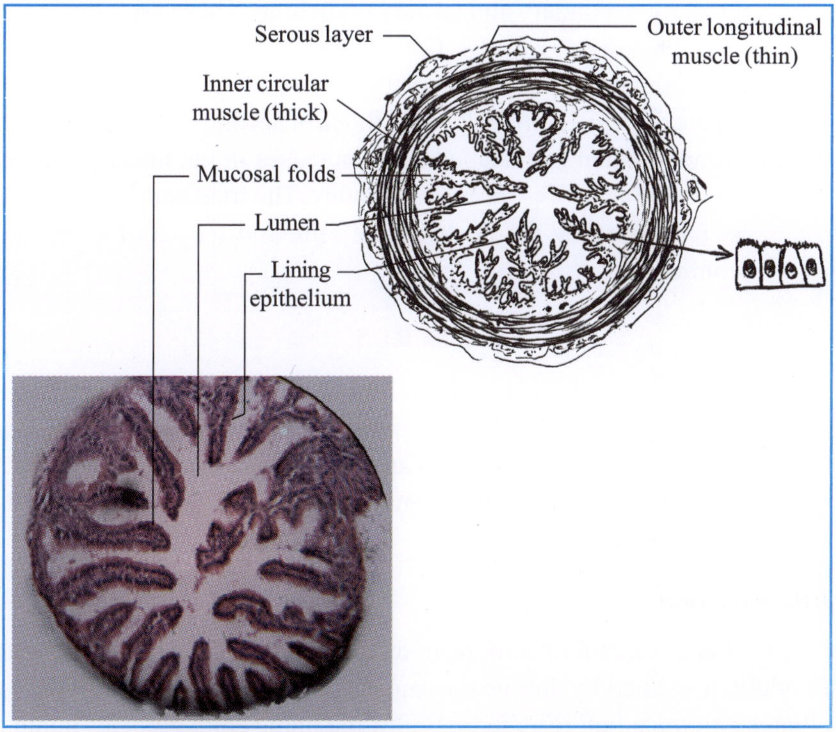

Fig. 8.11 Fallopian tube (transverse section).

1. Long mucosal folds are extended towards lumen. Few of them are branched ;
2. The mucous membrane is lined by simple columnar, containing both ciliated and secretory cells ;
3. Muscular coat is thin but comprises of inner circular and outer longitudinal muscles.

a) Outer serous coat – It is loose, thick and continuous with peritoneum and broad ligament.

b) The muscular coat consists of inner circular and outer longitudinal layers. The inner circular layer is thicker than the longitudinal layer. The muscular coat is thickest at the Isthmus and becomes gradually thin towards fundibulum.

c) Inner mucous coat – It is highly variable in structure at different level as well as in different stages of the cycle. The lumen of infundibulum and ampulla accommodate number of folds with primary, secondary and tertiary branching. These folds decrease in height towards isthmus. The lining epithelium is simple columnar type containing both secretory and ciliated cells. In the first half of the cycle cells are taller than those of second half. The number of nonciliated peg-shaped cells increases in the luteal phase of the cycle as well as during pregnancy. The transport of the ovum is facilitated by the beats of the cilia and waves of muscular contraction.

UTERUS

This is a pear-shaped hollow muscular structure meant for accommodating embryo or foetus and its covering membranes during the pregnancy. At the supero-lateral angles on either side it is connected to the uterine tubes. Ventrally it is communicated with the vagina through the cervical canal.

Endometrium

The mucous membrane of the body of uterus is called endometrium. In adults it is lined by simple columnar epithelium. This epithelium is ciliated columnar before puberty. Below the lining epithelium the lamina propria contains vessels, nerves embryonic stroma and numerous uterine glands. These glands are tubular, lined by simple columnar epithelium with occasional cilia and sometimes extend up to myometrium.

Changes occur in the endometrium in different phases of menstrual cycle. These phases are – a) Haemorrhagic (menstrual) phase, b) Regenerative (post menstrual) phase, c) Proliferative phase, d) Secretory phase and e) Pre-menstrual phase. The changes mainly occur in the

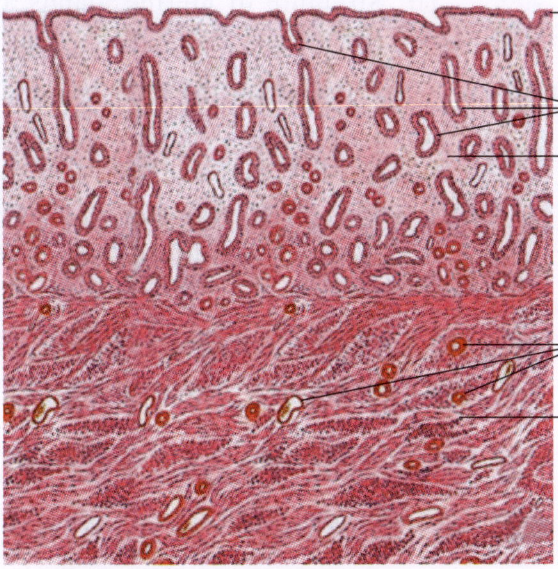

Fig. 8.12 Section of the wall of uterus (proliferative phase).

1. The cavity is lined by simple columnar epithelium ;
2. Lamina propria is thick and contains uterine glands and vessels;
3. Tunica muscularis is thick and contains many blood vessels.

superficial (functional) layer which cast off in each month during uterine bleeding. The deep (basal) layer remains unchanged and helps in the regeneration of functional layer. Out of average 28 days cycle, ovulation generally take place on 12th to 16th day.

The changes (average) which take place in the endometrium during menstrual cycle (28 days) are as follows :

I. Haemorrhagic phase : (Menstrual)

i) Period – 3 to 4 days

ii) Exfoliation of functional layer of endometrium takes place

iii) Uterine bleeding occur.

II. Regenerative phase :

i) Period – 1-2 days

ii) Epithelium is regenerated and lined by cuboidal cells. Thickness become 1-2 mm

iii) Structure of uterine glands are restored.

III. Proliferative phase :

i) Period – 10-12 days

ii) Growth of endometrium takes place. Thickness becomes 2-3 mm.

iii) Elongation of uterine glands and spiral arteries of basal layer occur.

IV. Secretory phase :

i) Period – 10-11 days

ii) Further increase in thickness of functional layer takes place

iii) The stroma cells enlarge due to appearance of cytoplasmic glycogen and lipid droplets

iv) Tissue fluid accumulates around the stroma cells

v) Implantation takes place if ovum is fertilised.

V. Pre-menstrual phase : (Ischimic)

i) Period – 1-2 days prior to onset of next menstrual discharge.

ii) Thickness of functional layer is reduced due to regression of C.L.

iii) Spiral arteries become shorten and more coiled

iv) Vaso-constriction followed by vaso-dilation and accumulation of pool of blood occurs in the lamina propria.

It may be noted that this cyclical changes in the endometrium occurs only between puberty and menopause. The duration of menstrual cycle may vary from individual to individual or even in the same individual.

Myometrium : The muscular coat is very thick and composed of bundles of smooth muscles, arranged in a thick inner circular and an outer longitudinal layers. In some places particularly in the body of the uterus, the inner layer contains few oblique fibers and show reticular arrangement. Large arteries, veins and lymph vessels are present within the deep (circular) muscular layer of the body. During pregnancy, these muscle fibers increase in number and size under the influence of oestrogen.

Perimetrium : It is derived from the peritoneum and covers the whole uterus excepting two lateral borders and some parts of cervix.

Cervix

It is covered by adventitia for most of the length. Dorsal aspect is covered by serosa. The tunica muscularis, particularly the circular layer is very thick and contains elastic fibers. The main bulk of cervix is composed of tough collagenous tissue containing little smooth muscle which changes it's character under the influence of hormones. The mucosa and sub mucosa form few large circular folds and numerous longitudinal folds, These longitudinal folds are associated with secondary and tertiary folds. Near the junction with the vagina, the epithelium is stratified squamous type. Cranially the cervical canal is lined by simple columnar epithelium. The glands of the cervical wall are mucigenous. These glands are branched, alveolar and lined by simple columnar mucous epithelium and open in the depression between ridges.

VAGINA AND VESTIBULE

The outer fibrous coat is called fascial coat since it is derived from the visceral layer of pelvic fascia. The muscular coat is composed of a thick outer longitudinal layer and a inner thin circular layer. The mucous coat possesses longitudinal folds and lined by stratified squamous epithelium. The lamina propria is composed of loose connective tissue and contains nerves, lymphatics and plexus of blood vessels. Glands are mostly absent. Lubrication of vagina is maintained by the mucus secreted from cervical canal.

The wall of the vestibule is almost similar to that of vagina. However, some sub-epithelial lymph nodules are present particularly in the wall close to clitoris. The wall also contains bilaterally placed compound tubuloacinar major vestibular mucous glands and some small branched tubular glands. The secretions of these glands provides lubrication to the vestibule. The major glands are homologue to the male bulbourethral gland and somthimes called ***Bartholine's glands***.

Vulva

The labia majora is covered by skin and possess fine hairs. However hairs are absent on the labia minora. Plenty of sebaceous glands are present. The hypodermis contains striated muscle the constrictor vulvae, blood and lymph vessels.

The mucous coat possess longitudinal folds and lined by stratified squamous epithelium. Glands are mostly absent.

BREAST

Mammary gland : Breasts are hemispherical or conical compound tubulo-alveolar glands of ectodermal origin situated in the superficial fascia of pectoral region. Each gland has a base, body and tip. The tip is popularly known as nipple. The gland is richly supplied with blood vessels, nerves and lymphatics but no fibrous capsule is found.

The glandular tissue consists of 15 to 25 lobes arranged in a radiating manner. Each lobe is composed of a number of *lobules* connected together by loose connective tissue and ducts. In a developed gland each lobule consists of a cluster of round or oval alveoli. These alveoli open into small lactiferous ducts which in turn joins with similar ducts to form the Lactiferous duct. Each of the lobes is drained by a single ***lactiferous duct***. These ducts converge towards areole and dilate to form ***lactiferous sinus*** and finally open on to the nipple. The pigmented circular area of the skin around the base of nipple is called ***areola*** which irreversibly darkened after first pregnancy. A number of modified sebaceous glands are found

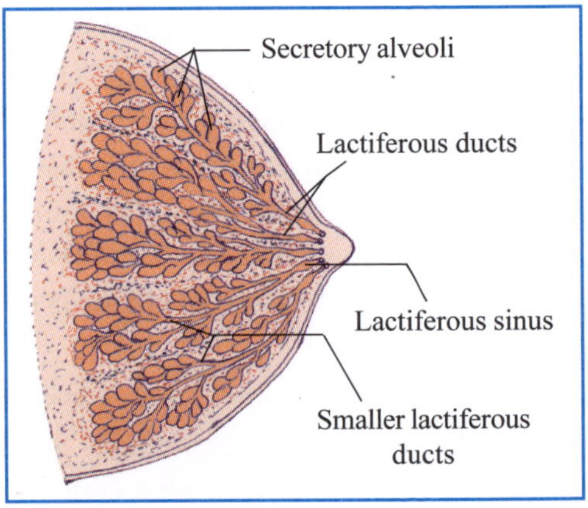

Fig. 8.13 Schematic diagram of developed mammary gland.

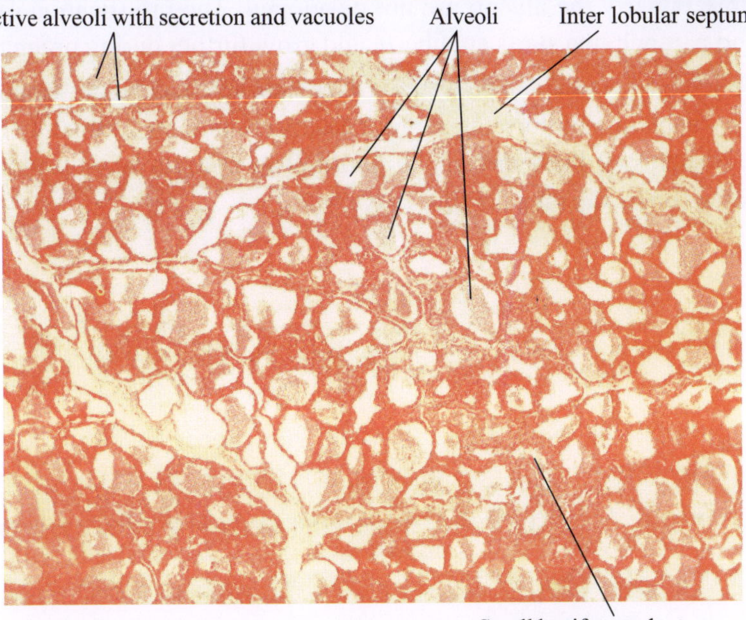

Fig. 8.14 Section of mammary gland.

1. Alveoli are of irregular shape and size ;
2. Interlobular septa are prominent ;
3. Few small lactiferous ducts are seen.

at the outer margin of the areola which secret a oily substance during lactation are called tubercles of ***Montgomery***. ***Nipple*** is a conical but blunt projection situated at the tip of the breast where the papillary part of the lactiferous ducts open. It contains longitudinal and circular muscles and supplied with plenty of nerves with sensory receptors for suckling.

The lactiferous duct is lined by simple cuboidal epithelium covered by myoepithelial cells. The lactiferous sinus is lined by stratified cuboidal epithelium and papillary openings are lined by keratinised stratified squamous epithelium.

Each duct divides into a number of terminal ducts which again give rise to numerous grape like secretory alveoli. During lactation, these alveoli are distended and lined by a single layer of cuboidal epithelium which is separated from the basement membrane by myoepithelial cells.

Before puberty the alveoli are not developed. The prolification of the gland parenchyma starts at puberty and grow further during pregnancy.

Each lobe is surrounded by a fibro fatty stroma which give support to the parenchyma by forming septa. These fibrous septa ultimately form the suspensory ligament of the gland. The contour of the organ is maintained by the inter-lobular fatty tissue.

9
ENDOCRINE GLANDS

PITUITARY GLAND (Hypophysis cerebri)

This reddish grey colored pea sized gland is situated in the sella turcica of sphenoid bone and connected to the 3rd ventricle at the base of the brain with a stalk called infundibulum.

It has following parts :

- Pituitary gland
  - Adenohypophysis (anterior lobe)
    - Pars distalis or pars anterior
    - Pars tuberalis
    - Pars intermedia
  - Neurohypophysis (posterior lobe)

Pars distalis

It is a bulky part situated in front of intraglandular cleft and consists of cells arranged in cords or clumps around sinusoids and supported by reticular framework.

- Cells of pars distalis
  - Chromophobes
  - Chromophils
    - Acidophils
    - Basophils

Chromphobes cells are comparatively smaller in size. The cytoplasm is agranular and takes light stain. They constitute about 50% of the cell population in pars anterior.

Acidophils are round or ovoid cells with centrally placed nucleus and contain eosinophelic granules in their cytoplasm. They take acid stain and appear pink in H & E preparations. These cells produce (a) growth hormone - STH (Somato trophic hormore) and (b) LTH (Prolactin or Lactogenic hormone).

Basophils are the largest variety of cells in pars distalis. The granules are smaller than those of acidophils and take basic stains. They stain darker with H&E. Basophil cells produce ACTH (Adrenocorticotrophic hormone), TSH (Thyrotrophic hormone), FSH (Follicle stimulating hormone) and LH (Luteinising hormone)/ICSH (Interstitial cell stimulating hormone).

Pars tuberalis

The parenchyma of pars anterior is extended upward around the infundibulum to form pars tuberalis. The cells are cuboidal in shape and arranged in clusters along the columns with elongated capillaries. Function of this part is not known.

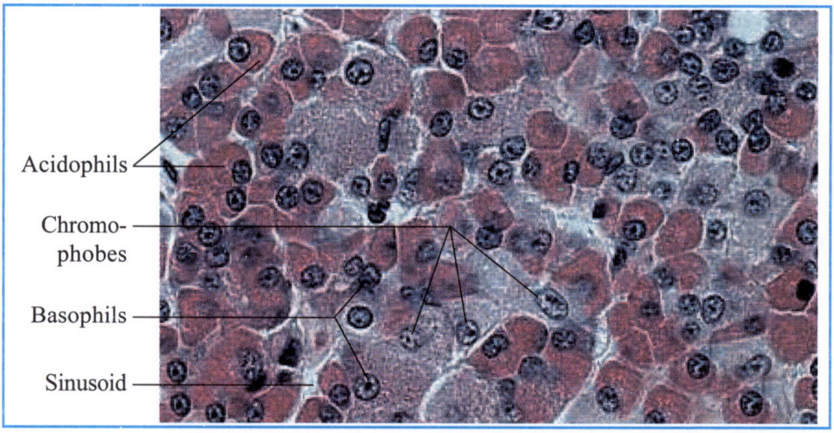

Fig. 9.1 Pituitary gland (pars anterior) showing different types of cells.

1. Acidophil cells (pink) are many ;
2. Basophil cells (blue) are clearly visible ;
3. Chromophobes cells (light) are plenty ;
4. Sinusoids are present between the clusters of cells.

Pars intermedia

This is a small strip of tissue separated from pars anterior by a cleft, the remnant of Rathke's pouch and remains in intimate contact with part nervosa. It contains small basophilic cells of polyhedral shape. They secret MSH (Melanocyte stimulating hormone). This part is better developed in lower vertebrates (fish and amphibians) and rudimentary in human.

Pars nervosa (Neurohypophysis)

This is the main component of posterior pituitary. The parenchyma of pars nervosa contains a special variety of neuroglial cells, the ***pituicytes***, non-myelinated nerve fibers and fenestrated plexus of blood capillaries. The axons of the cells of supra-optic and paraventricular nuclei of hypothalamus, pass along the pituitary stalk and terminate at the pars nervosa as bulbar expansions. ADH (Anti-diuretic hormone or vasopressin) and oxytocin produced in the cells of those nuclei pass through the axons in the form of secretary granules and stored in the bulbar expansions and thereafter released in circulation. These are called **Herring bodies**.

Therefore, the neurohypophysis does not synthesize any hormone but acts as a storage and releasing center.

SUPRARENAL (ADRENAL) GLAND

These are paired glands situated close to the cranial ends of the corresponding kidneys. Each gland comprises of an outer cortical part and an inner medullary part. Externally the gland is enclosed by a thick fibro-elastic capsule containing few smooth muscle cells. The reticular

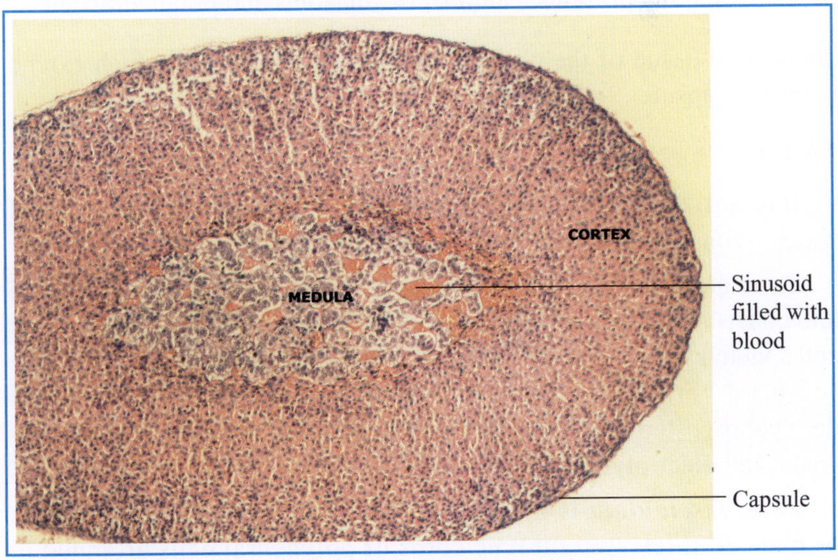

Fig. 9.2 Adrenal gland (low magnification).

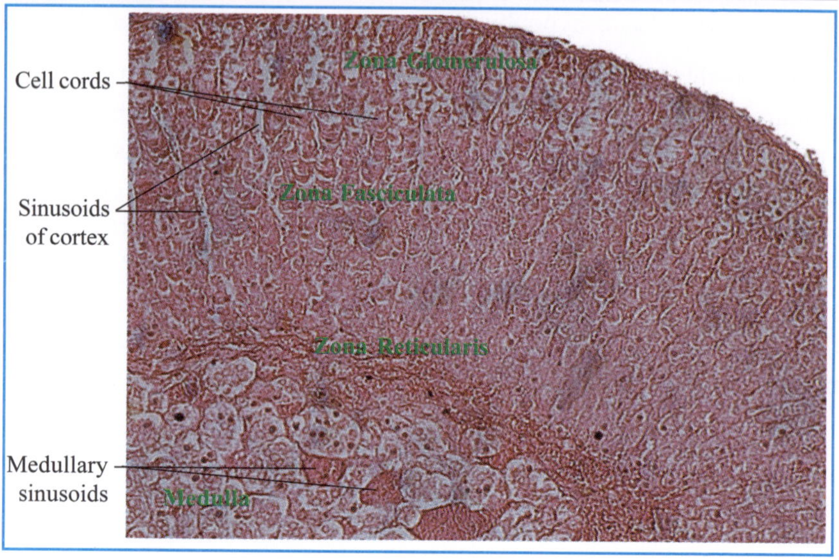

Fig. 9.3 Adrenal gland (higher magnification).

1. Three different zones in the cortex – Glomerulosa, Fasciculata and Reticularis are clearly observed ;
2. Cords of cells and sinusoids in between are prominent in the cortex ;
3. Medulla presents a number of sinusoids and polyhedral cells.

connective tissue of the gland is formed from the septa which extend from the capsule.

Cortex

It is derived from the mesoderm and comprises of three histological zones – zona glomerulosa, zona fasciculata and zona reticularis.

Zona glomerulosa is the thin outer zone situated below the capsule and consists of small polyhedral cells grouped around capillaries. Each cell contains deeply stained nucleus and basophilic cytoplasm. This zone secretes mineralocorticoid hormones (Aldosterone and deoxycorticosterone). These hormones are responsible for maintaining water and electrolyte balance.

Zona fasciculata is the thick middle zone and composed of one or two cell thick straight type cords of polyhedral cells arranged in parallel rows. Straight blood vessels and connective tissue elements are present in between these columns. This zone secretes glucocorticoids (Cortisone and cortisol) for maintaining protein, fat and carbohydrate metabolism.

Zona reticularis is the inner most zone composed of anastomosing network of cords of polyhedral cells situated around the sinusoids. Both dark staining and light staining cells are present. These cells secrete sex hormones.

Medulla

Except at the hilum the medulla is surrounded by cortex. It is composed of ovoid or polydedral cells arranged in groups or in anastomosing cords around wide sinusoids. These cells contain variable amount of secretary granules in their cytoplasm. These cells are also called Chromaffin cells because the granules take yellow brown colour when stained with potassium bi-chromate. This chromaffin reaction is due to oxidation of catecholamine (adrenalin and noradrenalin) present in the granules.

The gland is richly supplied with blood vessels. Numerous fine arterioles originate from the subcapsular capillary plexus and enter the gland through septa. These vessels pass between columns of cells and empty in the sinusoids of zona reticularis or in those of medulla. The prominent suprarenal vein situated close to the center contains muscle fibers in the adventitia along the length. Adrenalin and small amount of noradrenalin is produced by the medulla. The cortex is developed from mesoderm and the chromaffin cells of medulla are derived from neural crest cells.

THYROID GLAND

These are two highly vascular dark brown glands situated in front of the upper part of trachea. Both the lobes are connected across the midline by isthmus and form a H shaped mass.

The connective tissue framework is composed of the capsule, septa and interfollicular reticular connective tissue containing numerous blood vessels, nerves and lymphatics. The septa which extend from the capsule divide each gland into a number of lobules each of which contains a large number of follicles.

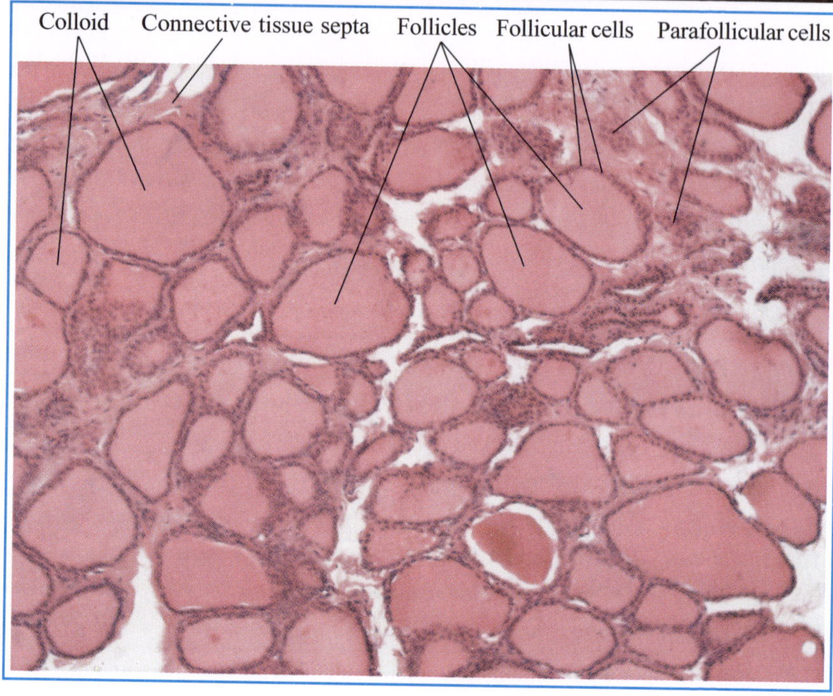

Fig. 9.4 Thyroid gland.

1. Oval or elongated thyroid follicles of various sizes are present;
2. Follicles are lined by simple cuboidal epithelium and filled-up by colloid substance ;
3. Few polyhedral or oval shaped cells are observed between some follicles represent parafollicular cells.

Follicles

These are irregularly spherical or oval structures of varying sizes situated within the lobules and are the structural unit of the gland. Each follicle is composed of a wall formed by simple cuboidal epithelium and the enclosed cavity generally remains filled with gel like substance called **Colloid**. In active stage the epithelial cells become columnar and colloid decrease in quantity. Microvilli and pinocytic vesicles are present on the luminal ends of these cells. The colloid contains Thyroglobulin which is rich in iodine. Golgi bodies, mitochondria, lysosomes and fagosomes are well visible under EM.

The gland secrets ***thyroid hormone*** which is responsible for normal growth and development of the body.

Para-follicular cells or 'C' cells are a second variety of cells remain in scattered form either in single between the basement membrane and follicular cells or in clusters between follicles. The cells are polyhedral or oval in shape and with acidophilic cytoplasm containing secretory granules. These cells secrete thyrocalcitonin, which maintain blood calcium level of the body. They are derived from the caudal part of 4th pouch (ultimobranchial body) of branchial apparatus.

PARATHYROID GLAND

These are two pairs (superior and inferior) of small glandular masses of yellow brown colour and situated close to the posterior border of each thyroid.

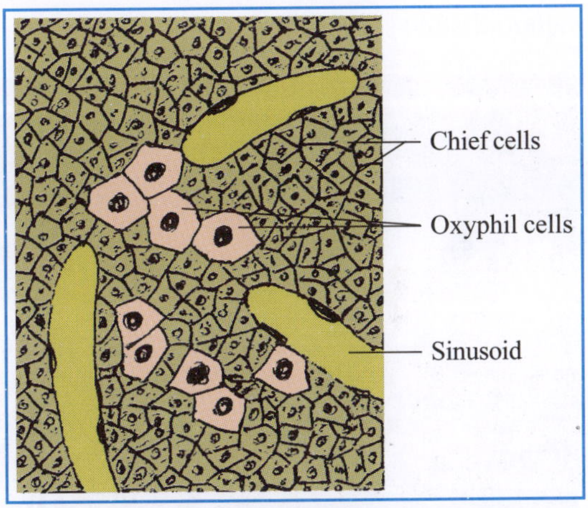

Fig. 9.5 Parathyroid (diagramatic).

The connective tissue framework is similar to that of thyroid but the lobules do not contain any follicle. The parenchyma is formed by the epithelial cells in the form of cords or clusters, placed around sinusoids. Two types of cells are found in these glands (a) ***Chief or principal cells*** and (b) ***Oxyphil cells***.

The chief cells are more in number. They contain clear cytoplasm and vesicular nucleus. Active cells contain ER and Golgi complex. The inactive cells are rich in glycogen. The chief cells secrete ***parathormone*** which is responsible for calcium and phosphate metabolism of the body.

The oxyphil cells are large and their cytoplasm contains acidophilic granules. Function of these cells are not known.

PINEAL GLAND (Epiphysis cerebri)

This is a cone or nodule like small body attached to the roof of third ventricle with a stalk. Fibrous capsule derived from piamater send septa inside the gland. This invation leads to the folding of the wall of the diverticulum and appears lobulated in histological sections. This lobular pattern is well marked in birds than that of mammals. The septa are richly vascularised. The main cells are the ***pinealocytes*** which have large nucleated body and long processes with club shaped ends remain in contact with blood vessels. Some supporting ***neuroglial cells*** are also present.

The brain sand (corpora arenacea) are irregular lumps of mineral salts (phosphates and carbonates of calcium and magnesium) are deposited in the connective tissue stroma of the gland. Pineal gland secrets melatonin and serotonin.

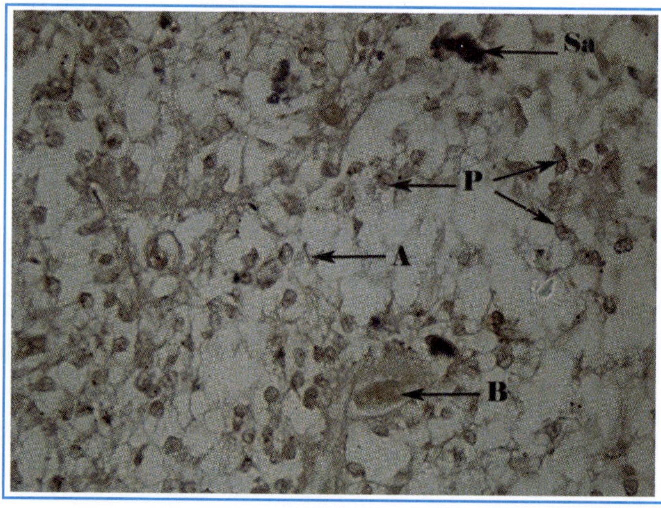

P – Pinealocytes
B – Blood vessel
A – Astrocytes

Fig. 9.6 Pineal gland (*Courtesy : Dr. Priyanka Minj*).

10

ORGANS OF SPECIAL SENSE

EYE

Cornea

This transparent membrane is composed of five layers of cellular elements.

Fig. 10.1 Cornea.

a) Corneal epithelium is composed of a thin stratified squamous epithelium which is continuous with bulbar conjunctiva at the periphery. This is about 5 cell thick. The epithelium regenerates rapidly and replaced continuously.

b) Anterior elastic lamina is a thin transparent membrane beneath the epithelium. It is composed of fine collagen fibers.

c) Substantia propria comprises of transparent bundles of collagen fibers and forms the bulk of the structure. Few cells with branched processes are present in this layer.

d) Posterior elastic lamina is similar to that of anterior lamina. At the sclerocorneal junction this lamina breaks up into bundles to form pectinate ligament which connects the sclera with the root of iris.

e) This is the mesothelium of anterior chamber made up of single layer of flat cells and remains attached to the posterior lamina.

Retina

It is composed of 10 layers of tissue elements out of which 3 layers are of nerve cells. These layers from outside inwards are as follows :

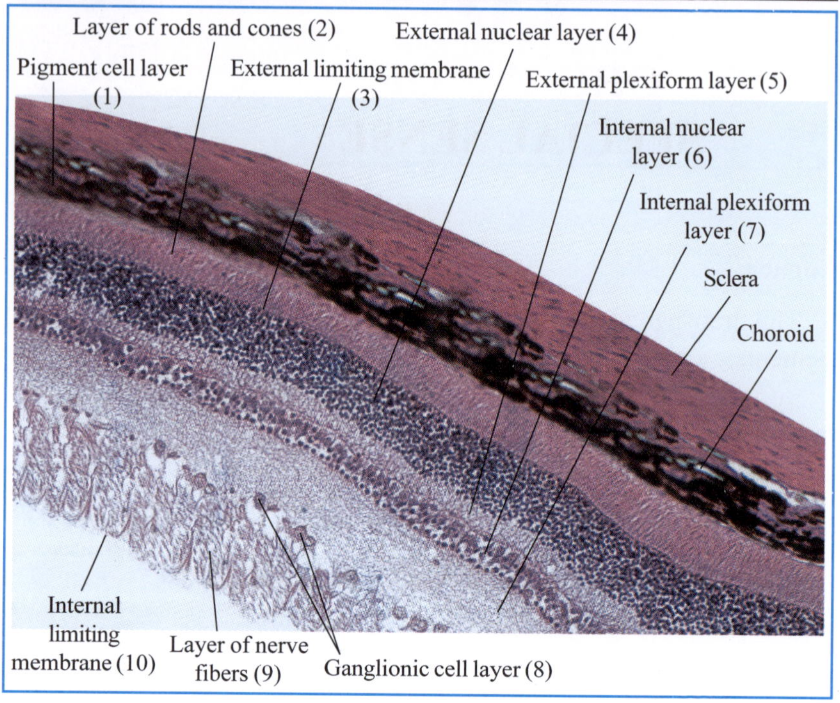

Fig. 10.2 Retina.

1. All the layers starting from pigment cell layer to internal limiting membrane are clearly observed ;
2. The neurons of ganglionic cell layer are prominent ;
3. External nuclear layer which appears to be granular is composed of cell bodies of rods and cones ;
4. Internal nuclear layer is composed of cell bodies of bi-polar neurons.

1. **Pigment cell layer** – This is the outermost layer and remains in contact with the choroid. It comprises of a single layer of cuboidal cells and each cell is attached to about 10 rods and cones. This layer reduces scattering of light within the eye ball.
2. **Layer of rods and cones** – The dendrites of the cells of outer nuclear layer have been modified to form the rods and cones. The rods are thin, long and contain rhodopsin. The cones are conical, thick and contain iodopsin. The rods are more in number than cones. The posterior part of the retina

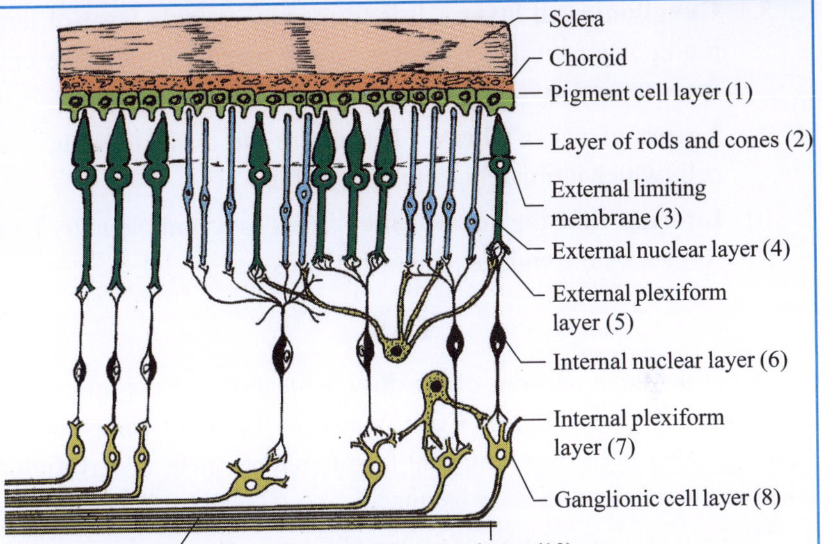

Fig. 10.3 Layers of retina (diagramatic).
(Retina is magnified many times in comparison to sclera and choroid).

contains relatively more cones. In the fovea centralis, the depressed central point on the macula lutae (yellow spot) contains only cones. Optic disc (blind spot) which is situated 3 to 5 mm towards the nasal side does not contain any rod or cone.

3. **External limiting membrane** – It is formed by the processes of the **Muller (glial) cells**.
4. **External nuclear layer** – It is composed of the cell bodies of rods and cones.
5. **External plexiform layer** – This layer is formed by the synapses between the central processes of the cells of rods and cones and the dendrites of inner nuclear layer.
6. **Internal nuclear layer** – It is composed of cell bodies of bipolar neurons and of modified neuroglial cells.
7. **Internal plexiform layer** – It is also a layer formed by the synapses between the axons of bipolar cells and dendrites of ganglionic neurons.

8. **Ganglionic cell layer** – It is formed by a single layer of large multipolar neurons. However, at the macula lutae these cells form several layers.
9. **Layers of nerve fibers** – It contains the axons of ganglionic cells which ultimately form optic nerve.
10. **Internal limiting membrane** – This is a homogenous layer formed by the ends of supporting cells.

EAR

Out of the three portions of ear, the cochlear part of the internal ear accommodates the organ of Corti, which is the main component of hearing. Other parts of internal ear (semicircular canals and vestibule) take part in maintaining body balance.

The cellular organisation of Organ of Corti is discussed here.

This organ is spirally arranged along the spiral lamina of the bony modiolus and within the membranous labyrinth. The membranous labyrinth remain within the bony labyrinth. The space above the Reissneis membrane is called *Scala vestibuli*, and below the basement membrane is known as *Scala tympani*. Both the spaces remain filled by perilymph. Scala media is situated between the two above mentioned spaces to form the long tubular cavity of the membranous labyrinth and remain filled up by endolymph.

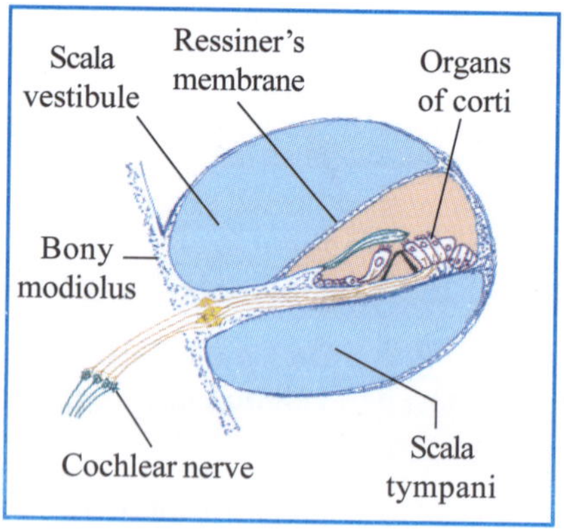

Fig. 10.4 Cross section of cochlear duct (diagramatic).

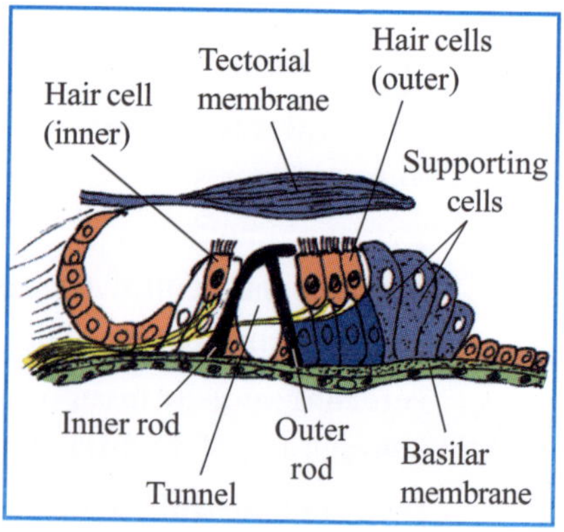

Fig. 10.5 Organ of Corti (diagramatic).

Organ of corti

It is composed of : 1) Hair cells, 2) Rods of corti, 3) Supporting cells and 4) Basilar membrane.

Hair cells

These are columnar cells and bear number of hairs (microvilli) on their free surfaces. They are arranged in a single row at the inner aspect of the inner rod and in multiple rows of 3 to 4 at the outer aspect of the outer rod. Their bases are attached to the supporting phalangeal cells which in turn are attached to the basilar membrane. The hair cells are innervated by cochlear nerve.

Rods of corti

There is an inner rod and an outer rod. They are widely separated at their bases but meet at their heads in a slanting manner. The bases are attached to the basilar membrane and thereby form the tunnel of corti.

Supporting cells

They are also called **phalangeal cells**. They are attached to the basement membrane and give support to the hair cells. The inner phalangeal cells are situated between the inner pillar and hair cells. Outer phalangeal cells are maintained in position by outer hair cells. **Cells of Hensen** are situated outside the outer phalangeal cells. These Hensen cells gradually become shorter and continuous with the **cells of Claudius** and thereby with epithelial cells which cover reminder of basilary membrane.

Basilar membrane

This membrane extends from the tympanic lip of osseous spiral lamina to the crista basilaris. Its innermost part, zona arcuata is thin and composed of small collagen like filaments. The outer part, called zona pectinata is thick and composed of an upper zone of homogenous layer of compact fibers, lower zone of compact bundles of longitudinal fibers and an intermediate structure containing few cells. The undersurface of the basilar membrane is covered by connective tissue containing blood vessels and some elongated cells.

Tectorial membrane

It extends from the outer border of spiral lamina and overhangs the hair cells. It is composed of delicate fibers embedded in a jelly like substance.

The stimulations which are created by the sound waves through various transmission media, are received by the peripheral process of the spiral ganglionic neurons from the hair cells.

This simulation is transmitted through the Cochlear nerve by the central processes of the said neurons and ultimately reach to the auditory area in the superior temporal gyrus of cerebral cortex.

INDEX

D

E

F

G

H

I

J

K

L

M

N

O

P

Q

—

R

S

T

U

V

W

X

—

Y

Z